WITHDRAWN

The
Weary
Falcon

BY TOM MAYER

Bubble Gum and Kipling
The Weary Falcon

The
Weary
Falcon

Tom Mayer

Houghton Mifflin Company
19 · Boston · 71

For the members of Frankie's House,
the actual and the honorary,
my friends all.
They lived the war,
and knew and understood it,
as well as anyone.

Contents

The
Weary
Falcon

"Falcon one five. Falcon one three."

"Falcon one five," Captain Slade said. "Go."

We were sitting in the revetments, with the turbines running, the rotors idling. Each blade made a separate whoosh, like a huge machete slashing through the air in front of your nose. Ahead of us was the strip and all along our side of it were rows of sandbag revetments, most with choppers parked in them. The ships that belonged in the empty ones were either down in Nha Trang for maintenance, or else had gotten zapped. There were Loaches — Hughes LOH–6s, to be proper about it — lots of UH–1H Hueys, Cobra gunbirds, and a few twin rotor Chinook troop carriers. Across the runway was a broad tarmac, with revetments around its edge for the olive or silver O–1 observation planes, and the control tower.

Falcon one three was Doug Mood, a Warrant Officer like me. He had been with us less than six weeks and had not gotten into any shit yet. He looked about seventeen, though he was twenty-one, and he wore his hair just a little too long for military taste. So did most of us Warrant Officers. We were pilots and very few of us were career. Mood was also trying to grow a mustache, but so far it just looked as though his upper lip were covered with egg yolk. He was a Loach driver. Loaches are very light observation choppers. We work them with only two men, the pilot and a gunner, though other outfits put a second gunner in back. Loaches are open-sided and have bubble noses and work in the treetops, like dragonflies or hummingbirds, and the pilot and gunner are very exposed. More Loach drivers get greased than any other kind.

"How about letting me take us out?" Mood said.

Mood stuttered a little, and was fairly sorry at radio work and navigation. Slade had taken him under his wing. Slade took all the new pilots under his wing. He was a four-tour hardnose — he had done three trips out here with the Special Forces — and looked like the ultimate Regular Army captain, but he was much given to advising the new pilots. He was not that good an airplane driver himself, maybe because he did not start until he was in his thirties. Maybe that is too old to learn. This was his last day flying. He had a week of processing and then he went home. I thought probably he and Mood had had a heart-to-heart about Mood's radio work and Mood was trying to come on all manly and gung ho, show he wanted to tackle the problem head on.

"You sure you can hack it?" I said.

"That's affirmative," Mood said.

"O.K.," Slade said.

The whole thing was like a college football scene. That is one incredible thing about the Army. It is amazing how many of them, even a lot of them who ought to know better, treat things like a football game.

For example, this morning's mission. The three of us were going on a sniffer mission. Sniffers are fancy smelling devices that are supposed to determine the presence of the enemy by sampling the air. Slade's Huey had one mounted. They are infamously sensitive to ammonia, which the artillery deposits in large quantities, and what we usually do is track last night's Harassment and Interdiction fire. Once we found a herd of monkeys. Slade was supposed to fly his Huey around a prescribed area and Mood's Loach was to check out any reading visually. I would fly around upstairs in circles and shoot up anything either of the others found. I am a gunship driver.

"I hope we find some shit," Mood had said at breakfast. "I'm due."

It was six-thirty and the eggs tasted like powdered cement. Our mess is the worst in the Nam — most people here eat fairly well — and the breakfasts are something else.

"We might," Slade said. "They've got an agent report. There's supposed to be a radio transmitter out there."

"Well," Mood said. "I'm due."

"Don't worry about it," Slade said. "You'll do fine."

"You better hope they don't grease your ass," I said.

Mood grinned, trying to show he thought I was just kidding, and Slade gave me a look that read don't shake the kid up. It was too early in the morning to get pissed off at such boy scout shit.

Now I ran my turbine on up to 100 per cent, checking it out, then back down to normal operating power, and tentatively eased up on the collective pitch control. The machine began to shudder tautly under me, to gather itself like a horse about to leap or buck.

"Fairway Tower," Mood said. His voice was carefully low pitched. Sometimes, in addition to the stuttering, you thought he was going to make adolescent frogs. "Falcon one three with a flight of three for takeoff."

"Falcon one three. Fairway Tower. The active is three four. Wind from three one zero at five. Altimeter is two niner niner niner. Density altitude is two thousand four hundred. Report hover check complete."

"One three. Roger that."

I did not pay much attention to the numbers. We fly these things out here by the seat of the pants. I lifted the collective a shade more and she came unstuck and I fed in left pedal to stop the torque. Hovering the birds out of the revetments is one of the trickier maneuvers. The bird is only a few inches off the deck with no transitional lift and she wants to bounce around like hell in the ground effect and the revetment walls look about six inches away on each side. It is a measure of our progress in this war that we still need revetments on a base we've held now in force for five years. I backed out without tangling up in anything and ran my hover check beside the runway.

"Falcon flight," Mood said. "All set?"

"Rog," I said.

"One five," Slade said.

Mood was a little ways down from me. He was holding his ship in hover, sliding back and forth a little. I could see his face clearly, except for the boom microphone across his mouth. He looked very tense. I thought he was probably practicing each transmission in his mind before he made it.

"Fairway tower. Falcon flight is ready for takeoff."

"Falcon flight is cleared for a north departure this time," the tower said.

Mood turned his Loach around and started down the runway, the captain trailing. I picked up to five or six feet and let the nose dip. She started forward, sinking slightly for a moment, the speed building rapidly, the runway blurring underneath, and I pulled up over our living compound; the trees and neatly spaced huts and a tangle of telephone and electric wires and a cluster of aerials like some weird spiked tree over the operations bunker skimmed under the nose. Several enlisted men standing in front of the mess hall waved.

"Falcon one three ba . . . ba . . . breaking right," Mood said.

"Sa . . . Sa . . . Say again?" I mimicked. It was impossible not to put the needle to him.

"Can it," Slade said.

We arrowed out across the base, at speed now, but still very low. The bird settled into its stiff flapping rush. Cobras are quiet helicopters, the pilots sealed in bubble fighter plane type canopies that they tint blue, but you still hear the little flap-pop and feel the jolt as the blade changes pitch.

We passed over the truck park and rows of armored personnel carriers and the officers' club with its patch of lawn and the long lines of barracks and a battery of howitzers in revetments. The roads shone blackly. They oil them every day and the surfaces, by noon, are an inky sticky slimy gumbo. Then the bunkers and concertina rolls and fighting holes of the green line slipped below and we turned the corner of the Hong Kong mountain.

Hong Kong mountain looms over the base. Beaucoup Americans have died on it and even though it is included by the perimeter and the infantry sweeps it regularly and they have a radar station on top we still get sniped from up there. It is honeycombed with tunnels. They try to dynamite any tunnels they find, but they never get them all. Personally, I think the inside of the mountain is hollow. One thing, you have to hand it to Charles — he will fuck your program any way he can.

On our left now was route nineteen. The brigade we're attached to is responsible for securing it, which means we spend a great deal of time flying up and down it. Ahead of us were the heavily lifting greenish-purple jungle mountains of the Mang Yang Pass. There is something sinister about them, about their color — it is too heavy, too dark, makes them feel like nighttime, or before a thunderstorm — and about the name too. Mang Yang. The first few times I heard it I thought it sounded funny, like a line in a joke about orientals, but if you say it over to yourself it

begins to sound mean. But of course now I know something about the place, which makes a difference.

I suppose I can thank Slade for some of that. I had been
in the Nam for almost a year before I met Slade, and he
was the first person I knew who did much history reading.
Of course all of us remember the places we fought and
went, the places where people we knew got zapped, or just
places that we operated in. But Slade was a bug on studying the French. He said you could learn everything you
needed to know from studying the French, and Mood was
interested in history too. He had done two years of college.

Anyway, the Mang Yang is one of the historic battle-
grounds of the war. Countless convoys have been ambushed there. The most famous one was French, an armor
and reaction force called Group Mobile 100. It had two
infantry elements, called the Korea Battalions because they
had fought there before they came here. When the
Americans first came, which was long before I did, the
roadsides were littered with fire-gutted French vehicles.
The VC used them for cover when they ambushed us, so
we towed the shells away, and we promptly tow away the
wreckage of our own vehicles when they get blown up,
which is frequently.

On the southern slopes of the pass is a cemetery for the
French dead. The enemy now uses the graves to launch
rocket attacks on the road, and we have burned and defoliated the vegetation all around it, but graves and tombstones make good cover. The same enemy, the 803rd Main
Force VC Regiment, that kicked shit out of Group Mobile
100 is still fighting us, though of course there are a lot of

North Vietnamese Army units around too. Slade took
Mood up there with a convoy one afternoon to look at the
place on the ground. I do not imagine there was much to
see but a bunch of craters. I have made rocket runs on it
twice myself, and we lost a Cobra there. The ship just
never pulled out of a run and both the pilots got greased.

We were skimming along the road, Mood ahead, then
Slade, and me last. I am supposed to stay high, but was
not. Cobras cost more than either of the other types and
the major does not like us to work them low. He has a hard
time explaining it when a Cobra goes in, which is certainly
not the case with a Loach. But I like sliding along just
above the grass, pulling up for trees and hills and banking
hard with the twists in the road. It is the best kind of
flying. It gives you a wonderful sense of freedom and
speed, of being able to go exactly where you want merely
by touching levers and pedals that are so responsive they
seem extensions of yourself. I never get tired of it.

We passed over guard posts manned by Vietnamese, and
they waved. The slopes are funny. As many birds as they
must have seen by now, and still they wave and jump up
and down like a bunch of cheerleaders. Then we went
over a company of Americans on a road sweep, two long
columns strung out on either shoulder, belts of machine
gun ammo slung around their necks catching the sun in
wicked glints, rifles held at the ready. They were walking
in a measured way, like somnambulists, the gait of working
infantry, one foot in front of the other and harness biting
into your shoulders and sweat in your eyes, and they did
not wave or even glance up. They lived in fire bases with

names like Strongpoint Five, or Strongpoint Action, miserable collections of barbed wire and dust and heat and sand and rats placed at intervals beside the road. Links in the mighty effort to keep open the vital artery to the central highlands is how the brigade magazine described them. I pity the poor bastards. Ducks in a shooting gallery. If Charles doesn't get you, you stand a fine chance of going bug fuck.

The trees had been cut back several hundred meters on either side of the road and the woods beyond were defoliated. The bare, dying trees were a dusty white, something like an aspen forest at home in midwinter. An artillery strike was going in on a ridge. Several white phosphorus rounds, markers, blossomed like evil flowers above the trees, then a line of orange flashes that instantaneously turned into angry balls of black smoke, the high explosive. They were shooting pretty close to the road, which meant something down there had gotten hit. I thought they might divert me for a run, but nobody said anything. I felt a tremor run through the ship as the concussion waves from the HE caught up with us.

Then we were in the Mang Yang, wheeling across the churned-up cemetery into our area. I knew Slade would be telling his crew chief, a sergeant named Rodriguez, to turn on the sniffer, and I climbed. A Cobra will climb like a scared baboon. One thing about Slade, he was reasonable. He did not care where I flew as long as I was in position to cover him if he hit anything.

The Loach and the Huey ran up a narrow valley, the mountains almost hanging over them on the east side.

The jungle below had not been defoliated, or, if they had tried, it hadn't taken. It was a solid canopy of murky green. I really had to watch not to lose them against it. The only breaks were occasional bomb craters or tiny abandoned Montagnard fields. At the corners of the fields were the remains of huts, hootches we call them, burnt-out thatch and frameworks of charred poles leaning at crazy angles.

I thought how it would be down there. When I first came to the Nam, almost twenty-two months ago now, I was a gung ho little dip. I wanted to see it all, know everything there was to know, and I wangled my way out on a couple of operations with the grunts. We were based down near Pleiku then, a brand new unit. They didn't have any housing for us, only tents, but at the time we thought that was fine. We all had John Wayne complexes. During the monsoons we fucking near drowned.

Anyway, I went out, and the jungle was unbelievable, really weird. You never saw real daylight. The light was always opaque. It was like living under water, like living at the bottom of the ocean. A huge gigantic snarl of vines and underbrush. And it smelled too, dank, stale, airless, like a cellar that hasn't been opened for years and years. You wondered how it could be so hot in such an infinity of shade, but it was. You sweated quarts, literally, in less than an hour, and you were always thirsty, always drinking and taking salt tablets. The grunts just dropped the tablets in their canteens, but I couldn't do that, it tasted like sea water. You could feel your insides, some fluid far more precious than plain sweat, draining out at each step, every time you moved. Everything rotted. Clothes, webbing, flesh. Thorn scratches festered within a few hours and were open running jungle sores or boils within days.

Sometimes when I thought about Slade going through that for three tours I wondered at him. He must have been a real fire eater at first. He did one tour in Laos and two in this asshole of creation. He had a Silver Star and two Bronze Stars and had been wounded twice. He never talked much about it, unless some old Special Forces buddy happened around, and then he and the buddy would go off and talk for hours.

One time I was in his room when he wasn't there hunting for something to read. He had a pile of magazines and at the bottom was an old *Infantry Journal*, with an article about him. The issue was devoted to ambushes, how to spot them and break them and how to set them up, and there was this long article about one he had pulled. The Perfect Ambush. Picture of him all strong jawed and spit and polish, beret cocked just right (those Forces cats spend hours each morning in front of the mirror trying for the right angle) and some dingus general pinning a silver star on him. His first name was Theron, which I had not known before. He was from Georgia and had one of those southern names that sounds like his mother was hung up on rare birds.

He and some of his boys had lined a trailside with ballbreakers, anti-personnel mines that pop up to the right height and spit out steel pellets, and had set up an L of sixteen claymores. They had blown the claymores all at once, killed half an NVA company. The article was typical

Army magazine, talked about what an astute student of enemy tactics Slade was, how he'd used his intelligence and worked up a careful plan and all that eagle scout shit, but you could imagine how it really must have been.

Eight scared pissless dudes. Four dinks and the Americans not sure of the dinks. They waited fourteen hours before the gooks walked into it, fourteen hours afraid to cough or scratch your balls or fart and rolling on your side to piss, and finally, when you were numb and your legs were completely asleep, they had come, two point men a hundred meters ahead of the rest. The point men were walking carefully and alert, and Slade must have had some hairy moments wondering if none of his boys had a foot sticking out, hoping the branches he'd cut to cover the claymores looked authentic, wondering if he'd camouflaged all the wires well enough, and maybe the point men stopped for a minute while one lit a cigarette, and you can be sure Slade's pucker factor must have been pushing maximum redline.

Then they moved on and the main body came, a company plus, more than a hundred men, bunched and chattering and anything but prime examples of silent jungle fighters, rifles slung, conical hats and packs festooned with shrubbery, camouflage, some pushing bicycles with mortar base plates and other heavy stuff. They kept coming until he could see the sweat stains dark under the armpits of their khaki shirts and maybe one had a gold tooth and the bike tires had red sidewalls, and Slade took a deep breath and blew the claymores, an incredible shattering road, bodies and bicycles and equipment broken and tossed like straw toys in a monsoon. Then he and his people would have run for it, maybe fired off a clip on full auto and headed for the hills, legs working fine in spite of being asleep. As they moved off through the jungle they heard new explosions as some gook tripped off a ball-breaker. The magazine was about to fall apart and had thumbprints all over the pages.

"One three, one five," Slade said. "We've got a reading."

I could not see anything down there but trees. Mood was a couple of hundred meters behind Slade and they were both making eighty knots or so. I was flying circles above them.

"Mark," Slade said. "Mark . . . now."

Slade's Huey broke to the right and Mood slowed down, came to a hover over the trees. His rotor wash beat into the foliage, parted the top layers.

"See anything?" Slade asked. He had climbed and was circling the Loach.

"Negative on that. Just a lot of trees." Mood was twitching the Loach around.

"Redleg again," I said. Redleg is artillery.

"Make sure," Slade said. "Run over the area again."

"One three. Roger that."

For maybe five minutes the Loach hovered and darted and shifted. The gunner was leaning far out the left side, his machine gun under his arm. Finally Slade said, "All right. Let's move it on."

"What a goatfuck," I said.

We took up formation, the Huey bobbing along above the jungle roof, jinking now and then to confuse any sniper

or antiaircraft gunner who might be drawing a bead, the
Loach in trail, me above. Slade got a couple more readings but as usual they didn't come to anything. Most of
the time here nothing happens. You go out alert but you
can only stay that way so long, no matter how hard you try.
Slade was always after us to stay awake. We did find one
very old hootch hidden at the corner of a clearing. Mood's
gunner dropped an incendiary grenade through the roof,
which immediately burst into bright flames. Gray smoke
eddied up through the trees. In accordance with form,
Slade called base and told them we had destroyed one
military structure. Which was a joke, but looks good on
troop and squadron and brigade reports. I doubted if
anybody had spent a night there in years. And if you
wanted to build a hut like that it would take you about a
half hour.

But mostly we just flew in erratic lines, back and forth
across the area, working gradually toward home. We had
been up an hour and a half and we were all tired. I was
thirsty and thought how good a beer or a Coke would be.
We are not supposed to drink beer until after last flight
of course, and usually no one does. Alcohol, even beer,
does not mix too well with flying. And it puts the major
very uptight. Anyone else but Slade would have figured
we were going to go zero for the morning and fudge a little,
but he kept at it.

The country below was more open, steep hills covered
with elephant grass and bamboo. There were a number
of trees, but it was no longer matted jungle. The grass was
cut by trails but Mood said so far none of them showed

signs of use. Which may or may not have been the case. Mood was still new. The experienced Loach drivers can tell you within ten minutes when a buffalo turd was dropped. But Slade's equipment wasn't picking anything up either.

The entire zone was a free fire area. That means a place where aircraft and artillery can shoot on sight or suspicion without clearing with anyone. In some areas it is amazing how long it takes to get clearance. You have to clear with your higher and he clears with his higher who clears with the chief slope in the area, who invariably says don't shoot if it happens to be his rice crop that might get churned up, and if he does say shoot the gooks are long gone. The people were all supposed to have been moved out of this area. They were Yards, and all of them were supposed to have been relocated near the base, provided securable fields and houses. Anything out here was automatically assumed to be unfriendly. Of course Yards are semi-nomadic, and not too many of them read notices or maps.

I turned the bird over to the copilot and was daydreaming. It was easy to see the other choppers against the brown grass. I try to give my copilots a fair amount of stick time. The only thing more boring than flying a Cobra around in circles at three thousand feet is being a passenger in a Cobra flying around in circles at three thousand feet.

I was daydreaming of home. My father has a ranch, near Tucumcari, New Mexico. My mother split when I was six and my brother got killed riding a Brahma bull named Bluetail in a rodeo. When I was a kid I couldn't decide if I wanted to go on the rodeo circuit or be a pilot. For a while after my brother got it I had about decided on the circuit, but there was something about airplanes.

I remember Trans Texas used to fly DC–3s into the local strip a couple of times a week. They made their approaches right over our place and I would stop whatever I was doing to watch. My father would never even look up unless they spooked his horses. But I could not take my eyes off them, even though they were only beat-up old gooney birds. Of course I did not know a goon from a Phantom. I thought the sweep of the wings and the way the sun shone on the bare aluminum like quicksilver was the prettiest thing I ever saw.

Later I went to college for a year, but did not like it. I tried to get on with the airlines, but you had to have all the ratings and beaucoup hours and even then they were taking mostly military boys. I did not have enough bread to take beginning lessons. It is goddamn expensive. Which was how I came to join up. That and they were going to get me anyway, so I thought I might as well have some choice.

I was remembering being a kid again working down in the corrals with the smell of horses and manure and the horse sounds, maybe pulling the wires off a bale of hay and hearing the old goon turn final with engines throttled back and the flaps and gear extending and how I would drop the bale of hay or whatever I happened to be doing and watch. It would make a thickness in my chest. It was as if I wanted to be up there so much that I knew how it would feel without having actually done it, as if I had some instinctive knowledge of the sweat and oil and old leather smell of the cockpit and the wind hissing past the aluminum skin and the muted rumble of those big old radials.

Slade said, "One three. Mark. Mark where I am now. One water buffalo."

"I got it," I said to the copilot, and started down.

"One wa . . . wa . . . water buffalo roger," Mood said.

The Huey wheeled away. Slade was circling so his door gunner could cover Mood. Mood stopped over the buffalo. It stood still and I thought maybe it was tethered. I knew the rotor blast would be switching the grass against it. Its head was down and the thick horns curved up, and it swayed them from side to side.

"What's it doing?" I asked.

"Standing there," Mood said.

Chalk one up for him. The rotor wash flattened patches of grass. They changed color as they bent, darkened like wheat when the wind moves through it. I kept flying in circles, always ready to wing over into a run.

I was pretty sure there was more down there than the buff. Buffs are valuable beasts and you don't leave them to wander aimlessly around in a free fire area. I was also getting tight through my chest, developing the old familiar sweatiness of palms, half listening for the first pop-twangs of ground fire. I was out of small arms range, but try to tell your instincts that. Being shot at in a bird is always a little remote, sounds like some car backfiring up the block, unless and until you take hits. I have taken hits seventeen times and I had one bird really shot to shit and there was nothing remote about any of those times.

The rounds that scored sounded like very large hailstones pounding a tin roof and the ship shuddered, seemed to stagger in the air, as if it had met some invisible barrier. You curled yourself tightly into your armored seat, hunkered your head down until it felt as though your chin were part of your chest, and put your airplane through the wildest gyrations you could improvise and scanned the gauges. How you scanned those gauges. Then you were away from it and if you weren't out of control or on fire you headed home. The bad time I was flying a Huey Bravo gunship, a Hog, the type we had before Cobras, and I checked in back to see if my crew was all right. The right door gunner was dead, draped over his gun, his head and shoulders twisting in the slipstream. The round had pierced his plastic face visor and the material around the puncture was spiderwebbed crazily. I made myself turn around and lock on the gauges, strung tight as a rubber band at the snapping point as I waited for the outlet temperature to rise, or the per cent power needle to start unwinding, or for some new vibration.

"Ga . . . ga . . . ga . . . gooks," Mood was shouting.

"Take it easy," Slade said. "How many?" His voice was cool, conversational. You had to admire him. I can do the John Wayne bit on the airwaves as well as anyone when nothing is happening, but Slade never flustered.

"Two."

"Are they armed?"

"Negative. I mean I don't know. I can't tell. They're hiding in the grass."

"You want me to fire 'em up?" I asked.

"Negative, one one. One three, check 'em out. Watch yourself."

Slade was really a mother hen, at least with Mood. I wished we knew whether the gooks were armed or not. They probably weren't soldiers. Soldiers would know better than to walk along a trail in that area in broad daylight with a large and conspicuous animal. That they were hiding meant nothing. Armed choppers shake people up. I have been shot at by ARVN, our noble allies, more than once, and nobody in his right mind, innocent or not, is going to advertise his presence with a Cobra around in a zone that is even slightly dubious.

They might be stray Yards or members of a press gang. The bad guys used Yards or anybody else who happened to be handy as porters or to build fortifications. But still they might be gooks. Charles fucks up as often as we do, dies just as often for making stupid mistakes. If those clowns were armed all they would have to do was roll over and put a burst into the under belly of Mood's Loach. It was about as fat as the Goodyear blimp from their vantage point, and just as vulnerable.

Slade was the one who had to make the decision. He was running the show. Most commanders would have zapped them straight off, worried about who they might be afterward. But Slade was famous for trying to make sure. That was excellent tactics — you didn't win a war like this by shooting people who might be on your side —

but it was often dangerous. He didn't have much time. I thought he was probably considering going in after them himself, bringing them back to base in his Huey. Then the problem solved itself.

"They're running," Mood said. "They're DD-ing."

"Are they armed?" Slade asked.

"I can't t-t-t-tell."

"O.K. Fire 'em up," Slade said.

I couldn't see them. The grass was too high. The buff was standing in the trail. Mood was flying sideways to give his gunner the maximum field of fire. I could see the tracer arcing into the grass.

"Two gooks greased," Mood said.

"You sure they're dead?" Slade asked.

"Affirmative. Not even twitching. You want us to grease the buff?"

"Check the bods out first," Slade said. "Check for weapons."

"Roger that."

The Loach worked over the area again, but found no weapons, not even any bunkers. There are about ten bunkers per mile along most trails. The gooks duck into them whenever they hear us coming. Mood said he thought one of the bods looked like a woman, but he could not be sure without landing, turning it over.

"Can you get down?" Slade asked.

"She's under that big ass tree over there."

"Over where?"

"Sorry. To my nine o'clock."

"O.K. But watch yourself."

Mood landed near the tree and his gunner got out, disappeared into the grass. In a minute he was back and Mood lifted off.

"It was a woman," he said. "One dink female. She had a military ra . . . ra . . . rucksack."

"Did your gunner recover it?"

"Negative."

"Why not?"

"It was shot up. But it was a military rucksack."

The gunner had not wanted to fool around with a bod. Slade didn't say anything for a while. Then he told Mood to shoot the buff. I could see the tracer flicking into the beast. It plunged and bucked and then lay thrashing in the grass. It must have been tethered. I made a low pass over the area, low enough to spot the bodies. Both wore black pajama clothing and were sprawled face down. Even from only twenty-five feet they looked more like broken toys, discarded dolls, than people.

We flew directly down the road on the way in. Mood was running in front, maybe five or ten feet above the pavement. He lifted the ship over trucks and jeeps and dipped down again, scattered a trio of civilians walking along the roadside and made a bicyclist veer into the ditch.

"Well, one three," I said. "You lost your cherry." I made it as sarcastic as possible, but I do not think he noticed.

"Roger that. One five, you want me to call us in?"

"Affirm." Slade sounded tired.

Ahead of us was Hong Kong mountain and the wire of the green line. There were fields and people working in them and a convoy on the road. We slanted away from the road. The people in the fields were dressed the same as the ones we'd just killed. We went low over some huts. Two small boys, both bareass naked, were playing in front. They waved at us, jumped up and down.

"Fairway International," Mood said. Fairway International instead of plain Fairway Tower is the way we call up when we have kills. It tells everyone what we have done. It is the same as a fighter jock doing victory rolls, and is a custom here, although I have no idea how it started. "This is Falcon one three with a flight of three five to the November Echo. Landing."

I loosened my seatbelt and twisted around. It didn't help much. All the crap we wear, pistol belt and flack vest and the harness, loosening the belt does not make much difference. I had some gas and the beginnings of the runs. It was probably the magnificent lunch we had. It is a well-known fact that our mess sergeant is employed by Hanoi. Lunch was fried spam and dumplings the shape and consistency of dog shit. It was just a half hour since we had eaten, and maybe I would have been all right if there had been time for a nap before this afternoon show. The slopes on both sides stop the war for a few hours after the noon meal, which is the way to do it. But some higher wanted another area reconned by sniffer, so here we were, flapping along toward the Mang Yang again.

Mood was ahead again, flying a little more conservatively than he had on the way in, then Slade. They had given

Mood a lot of gas before lunch. We landed and debriefed and then went over to the compound, sat under the shade trees in front of the bar with soft drinks. I got there last and caught Slade with a beer. He was standing by the refrigerator, his back turned, but I know he had a beer. He tried to hold it so I couldn't see the label, like a kid caught stealing candy. Maybe at first he thought I was the major. In any case it was unlike him and I had to laugh. Spit and polish by the book Slade. The only man in the troop who spit shined his own boots. He killed it and dropped it in the trash can and opened a grape.

Outside Mood was telling what had happened, trying to be modest about it. He was grinning shyly, coming on like an ace sophomore quarterback with reporters. I imitated how he sounded, ga . . . ga . . . ga . . . gooks, and everyone laughed, including him, as if it was all part of some friendly fraternity initiation. Slade sat there quietly. Then Major Folsohm came by and patted Mood on the shoulder. You could see Mood's ego swell like a weather balloon when they put the helium to it.

That was the way it always was, of course. I remember the first major we had, the one in command when we got there, used to say, "Good morale is when you kill people." He was a West Pointer. It was something I took for granted at first, I suppose. You got kills, and even if your unit took casualties, as long as you felt you had done all right yourself, there was the lift afterward. Part of it was release from tension. You wound up tight when the shit was hitting the fan, the first times because you did not know what it would be like, and then, later, because you did know what it would be like, so that when it was over and you were back where it was safe, or at least familiar, you felt high, almost like you were out on a pisscutter with the first three drinks down and making a lightness, a glow in you. And of course with Mood this morning there was the acceptance bag, the initiation thing.

I remembered how it had been my first time and I was no better or different than Mood. I had really wanted the hunter image. When we first came, in Pleiku, I had named my ship *The Psychedelic Killer* and I got one of the maintenance sergeants to put a psychedelic paint job on a spare helmet. By orders all helmets were supposed to be OD, but whenever we were going someplace with no highers along I would wear my painted one. That was when we were flying Hogs and my crew really dug it.

The first kill I got made me. The country around Pleiku is open, reminds me of home. Lots of grazing grass and long fence lines and rolling pasture land and clear air and the mountains on the horizons are blue. One afternoon we surprised a squad out in the open. That does not happen often, but we caught them humping along through some elephant grass. They had rucksacks and a couple of automatic weapons and they were dressed in an assortment of clothes, black pajamas and parts of uniforms. At first we thought they were Popular Force troops. PFs dress about like that too. But base said there were no friendlies in the area and about that time they began shooting at us.

We made gun runs and got most of them on the first pass but this one cat split off through the grass for the jungle. The jungle was at least four kilometers away but he went pumping off for it. We made a pass and the flex guns jammed and the gunner missed him. I came back around. He was still running in a straight line for the jungle. I let go one rocket and it hit square between his legs. We could not even find any pieces. The major, the first one, was with us and he flew over and said, "Now that's what I call overkill."

That night we went up to the Air Force officers' club, almost every pilot in the troop, and got incredibly pissed. We sat bullshitting for hours and I am sure I looked and acted just like Mood this morning.

But it does not work on me like that any more. It certainly did not this morning. All we'd done was blapped a couple of Yards. I was sure of that. They were probably lost, or maybe lived up in the back country and didn't know they were in a free fire zone. Or even if they were working for Charles what we had done made no real difference except to the people who were dead. Slade felt the same as me. Mood was saying he thought they must have been couriers.

"Don't be a dickhead," I said. "They were probably just Yards."

"I doubt that," Major Folsohm said. If they were innocent civilians he could not report them as kills. Majors get promoted by the number of gooks their boys kill. The major did not care for me anyway — he wrote on one of my reports that I showed insufficient respect for the traditions of the service.

"Couriers don't walk around with buffs, sir, and they do carry weapons," I said.

"Maybe they threw them down," Mood said. "Anyway they were in a free fire zone."

"What difference does that make if they weren't gooks?" Slade said.

"If they weren't gooks," Mood said, "how come they ran?"

"Maybe they were scared," Slade said. "Maybe they had a notion we were going to zap them."

Coming from Slade, that really stopped the conversation cold for a bit. Finally the major said they were gooks or they wouldn't have been where they were. Mood sat there grinning still, but working at it now, and the major was looking at Slade as if he had just noticed Slade had spots, or leprosy. We drifted off to lunch by twos and threes.

Now I thought Slade really was different. When I first knew him I thought he was just a typical hardnose, Regular Army, career, like the rest of them but maybe a little smarter than most. A lot of the old pros are smarter than you think at first, which explained his interest in the French. They make them study stuff like that in the Forces. But RA types never cross their highers. Highers write your efficiency reports and if you are a lifer your efficiency reports mean everything.

Slade had come up through the ranks, of course, or he would have been more than a captain. He told me once he joined when he was sixteen, lied about his age. He was airborne, always wore the jump wings with wreath and star of a master paratrooper under his pilot's wings, and a Combat Infantry Badge with a star for Korea under that. He also wore the Forces insignia on his right shoulder still. I assumed he had learned to fly because he had gotten tired of humping the boonies, which showed some intelligence, but not too much, or he would never have humped the boonies in the first place. Not three times anyway.

But there were other things. As I said, he took care of the new kids as best he could, which was unusual, and he went to church once in a while, which almost nobody else in the troop did, and he did not go to Sin City, which everyone else did religiously. Sin City was the prostitute's compound, run by the ARVN. When the 1st Cavalry was here, they started it, so they could keep the VD rate down, but it got in the papers and all the mothers back home got uptight and wrote their congressmen and the Cav gave it to ARVN. We all went down there except for Slade. He was married and had two kids, but so were a bunch of the other officers, and I never noticed that stopping any of them. In fact, the married ones were usually the chief rutters. Maybe they missed not having it regularly more than the rest of us.

We turned away from the highway and headed for our area, on the other side of the road from this morning. It was hot and fairly turbulent. Mornings and evenings are the good times to fly, the first mission and last light. The Mang Yang had changed color. The deep purple had washed to a dirty blue. Fat white cumulus clouds were building at three thousand feet or so. You could actually see them expand. In several hours they would be thunderknockers.

We had five readings but they didn't turn up anything, not even a hootch. I let my copilot fly. I felt worse. I had never been sick in an airplane before, never even came close except once, and that was under very different circumstances. I pulled my sun visor down, which cut the glare, and shut my eyes for a few moments.

I thought back to the bad time, for that is how I remember it, though I have gotten so that I can consider it without the process shaking me up. During Tet of '68 when the shit was really flying in Hue they moved us up to Phu Bai, a camp outside the city, to help out. We did not take much, just toilet kits and change of clothes and whatever else we could cram under the seat, and flew the birds up there one morning and that afternoon we were making runs on the Citadel. Tet was bad all over the country but it was worst in Hue. I flew sixty-one hours in ten days. Usually you don't fly a hundred hours a month.

They rocketed us fairly regularly and none of the roads were secure and flying over the city itself was an experience. Kennedy International would seem like a quiet country airstrip in comparison. You never saw so many birds. Gunbirds and Medevacs and O–1 spotters were weaving around all the time, and Marine H–34s and Skynights, and at least once an hour the Air Force ran a strike with F–100s or Phantoms, or else the Marines did with Phantoms or A–4s, and then Vietnamese would show up in their Spads and nobody could talk to them. You could count on one near miss midair an hour and we all felt the slope pilots were much more interested in shooting us down, or ramming us, than hitting Charles. We had Hogs still and one of my gunners kept shooting at the Spads.

And ground fire. You never saw ground fire like that.

You took hits almost every time you went out. The fourth mission I went on was the time they really fucked us over. The ship had so many holes we could not count them all and my right door gun's helmet, behind the crazy spiderwebbing of the visor, was full of runny brains and my copilot got a splinter in the foot. At that we were lucky.

But the bad time was after things started to settle down. The NVA units, except for the one in the Citadel, withdrew across the river and started pulling back up along The Street Without Joy and into the Ashau. We got some of them, but I personally think most of them got away. The grunts began running sweeps up and down the Street again, trying to open and secure it, and it was on one of those that my bad time happened. An airborne unit took some sniper fire from a village up on the Street and they called us in to zap the vil.

When we got there the troops were pinned behind a dike off to the roadside and we made our runs parallel to them. If you make your runs parallel to the friendlies there is considerably less chance of dinging a few by mistake. It still happens, of course, but not as often. We expended into the village. I set a couple of hootches on fire with rockets and I laid one in a bunker opening. I am a very good shot with rockets, but to put one right down a bunker opening was outstanding.

We went on back and rearmed and then came back up to the vil. The troops were in the vil. Anyway they weren't still pinned down behind the dike. A pair of Medevac Hueys was landing near the treeline. From that I figured the grunts had taken some wounded. Our flight leader called up the ground commander and asked him if he wanted us to make some more runs.

"Negative. We need more Medevacs. We got beaucoup dinged civilians down here."

"We are not Medevacs," the flight leader said.

"Understand not Medevacs. We need Medevacs. We got wounded lying all over the place down here."

It was the oldest story in the book. The gooks put a sniper or two in the trees near a vil, usually without telling the villagers, and then when we take fire we dump all available shit on the place. Afterward we try to tell the civilians it only happened because they let the gooks into the vil to begin with. I doubt if the civilians see it that way. And what could they do? Charles sneaks in and climbs a tree, or comes in and points his gun at you and tells you he'll zap you if you breathe a word and then climbs the tree.

Our flight leader and the ground commander talked some more and the flight leader ordered us in to help pick up the wounded. It was awful. There were at least a hundred dead and wounded. The grunts kept finding new ones. The vil must have been absolutely full of people. Every house and bunker must have been crammed. Probably lots of them were people who had been run out of Hue by the fighting there.

We made three trips. They loaded us with women and children and old men. Some of them were crying and all of them were bleeding and most were in shock. We could never get the bird really clean afterward. But the worst thing was the second time we went in. They had the wounded in groups around the LZ and the medics were working on them and the grunts were standing around watching. We set down and right ahead of me were a bunch of kids. They were all dead or hurt. One was a little boy of maybe seven and his arm was shot off. He was screaming and you could see the blood spurting out where his arm had been. I couldn't hear the screams because of the turbine noise and my helmet, but you could see his mouth open and his eyes screwed up and his chest heaving. They were loading us and this grunt walked over to the kids, shaking his head. He knelt down beside the little boy and patted his hair, pushed it back from his forehead. I doubt if the kid knew he was there. Then the grunt stood up and looked down at the kid almost tenderly, the way my father used to look at a sick foal, and shot him in the forehead. He turned away and looked right at me and shook his head again and walked away.

So that was my bad time. Whenever I would think of it for a long time I would get the cold sweats, and for the rest of the day it happened I flew around not sure of my stomach.

Shortly after the bad time, I extended, which may not seem logical. When you go in the Warrant Officer pilot program they make you sign on for five years. That is the price you pay for learning to fly. But what it means is that they are going to get more than one tour out of you. They have too much invested in you. I knew after the bad time that there was no way I would ever come back here once I left. I would go over the hill or do whatever I had to, but there was no way they could make me come back.

If you extend, you get it all over with at once. I did not even take my bonus leave between tours. When I finish up this tour I will go home and they will make me an instructor and I will figure out some way to get an early out. I keep getting bad reports, and I make it clear to everyone that I am no career type and they will not be able to send me back, so I think it will not be too hard to make them let me go.

Slade found a trail and followed it up a canyon, lost it in heavy jungle. There was a stream on the canyon floor and, since you usually find base camps and hospitals within a few hundred meters of water, Slade pulled up and had Mood do a visual recon. Nothing. Slade went back down, started following the trail in the direction we had come from, and a voice came over the emergency channel, very weak but clear.

"Anyone, Hawkeye niner, Hawkeye niner. We're hit. We're hit."

"Hawkeye niner," Slade said. "Falcon one five. Say your position."

No reply.

"One one," Slade said. "Did you copy that emergency transmit?"

"Affirm," I said.

Hawkeye was a call sign belonging to an Army bunch flying O–1s from An Khe Main.

"Keep monitoring," Slade said.

Slade called out operations and got grid coordinates for the area Hawk nine had been working. Base had heard

Hawkeye call up too, but the transmission was too short for a good directional fix. The O–1 did not call again.

"What is your fuel situation this time?" base asked Slade.

"Six zero minutes plus. My Loach element has slightly less."

"You're closest to him."

"Rog," Slade said. We were about thirty clicks from the general area. "I do not have enough fuel for a protracted search."

"Understand."

"We're on our way up there now." We had turned to the right heading and were climbing. "Suggest you get another flight up at the earliest possible."

"I wonder what got him?" Mood asked.

"Maybe nothing," Slade said, but I knew he did not believe it. He was protecting Mood again. Where we were going was way up in the high country, into the heart of Charlie's country, up where neither us nor the dinks nor even the French had operated much. Slade and I knew they had plenty of heavy caliber machine guns up there and even some light Czech antiaircraft stuff with radar fire control. Choppers are easy meat for AA and heavies. We don't get much of it down low, or where we can get artillery, because heavies are too bulky and heavy to transport. When they hit someplace where you can get back at them quick they travel light.

The country was rising rapidly. We crossed an intersection of two rivers, a lot of wild white water tumbling along a canyon. Above the junction the waters were deep flowing and smooth and green. Off to the left were some peaks that must have gone seven or eight thousand feet. They were draped with strips of gauzy fog. The jungle was wet green up here, like a mint bed. It wasn't dusty like the low country.

Some of the hills had been used for insertions and combat assaults. Their tops were tangles of shattered hardwood trees. Huge strips and javelins of wood were lying around. The Air Force has a special thousand pound bomb to blow LZs like those. But the jungle reclaims even the hilltops quickly. Vines and ferns curl up the stumps, bandage the scars with green, and ground cover edges over the lips of the craters.

We skimmed over a ridge line and below was the first of the valleys Hawk nine was supposed to have searched. It looked like something out of a tourist brochure for the man who wants to get away from it all. A broad high country valley, sealed on all sides by ridges, with a quick clear river curving through the middle. It looked like it ought to have trout. The water didn't appear deep and it eddied around large white boulders. At the lower end was a waterfall. The jungle roof was unbroken except for a few grassy spots on the riverbank. There weren't even any craters I could see, which was very unusual.

"I bet there's some tigers down there," Mood said. "I'd really groove a tiger skin. I can see it on my wall."

"Do your thing," I said. "You might get one. But they're harder to grease than buffs."

"I'm going to make some runs across here," Slade broke in. "If the Hawkeye aircraft is down there, snoopy ought to pick it up. One three, you go upstairs with one one."

"Why?" Mood asked.

"Because I said to."

Mood was really running for the daily blood and guts award. It is amazing what killing a woman or two will do for you. Slade was sending him up because it was safer. If Slade couldn't find anything with the gadget, he'd have to let Mood work out.

The valley ran from northwest to southeast. Slade wheeled the Huey up to the northwest end, turned against the ridge, dropping hard, and began a run. He was really moving out, doing quick little banks, dodging the higher treetops.

I had no big expectation that he was going to find anything. Aside from not trusting the sniffer, the chances were always against finding what you were looking for. Almost everything in this country happens by chance. The biggest kill we've had in the last six months happened when a pair of Cobras found a base camp by accident. They were bringing the payroll over from Pleiku, and they spotted some movement along a stream. Eighteen confirmed kills. If one of those Cobras had gone down you would have seen the most intensive search and rescue operation of the war.

I was not paying any attention to Mood. He was supposed to look out for himself and keep out of the way. Slade was really diddling the Huey around, and it was very hard to keep track of him against the jungle green. I have often thought they ought to paint the roofs of the Hueys and Loaches identification orange so we could see them. The only time the gooks see the roofs of our ships is when one goes down and flips over.

Slade was in the southeast end of the valley, banking over the waterfall. I was watching him and trying to spot likely gun emplacement sites. Charles learned a long time back not to use tracer on us. If you see tracer coming up from somewhere it is easy to douche the area down, so now you have to estimate the terrain, keep an eye on all the likely looking spots. Slade rolled out and ducked to one side and was picking up speed when I saw something out of the corner of my eye, some movement in the air that was abnormal and I laid the Cobra over. Mood was going down. The Loach was obviously out of control, almost tumbling down the sky. It hit and was thrashing, before I came awake enough to call Slade or even begin to be afraid.

"One five," I said. "Break right. Break right. They got one three."

Slade whipped over and began calling, "One three, one three, one three . . ."

"He's to your three o'clock low," I said.

"Where?"

"Twelve o'clock now."

Slade headed for him. The Loach was thrashing. Choppers usually don't go down like conventional planes, rarely die with a sudden crunch or an explosion, but instead beat themselves to death on the ground. They remind you of a headless chicken flapping away the last of its energy. One of Mood's blades sheared, cartwheeled above the jungle. It all looked like slow motion.

"Where is the fire coming from?" Slade asked.

"I don't know." I hadn't heard a single shot.

"Have you taken hits?"

"Negative."

"What was one three doing?"

"I'm not sure. I was watching you."

I was searching those ridge lines as hard as I ever did anything in my life trying to figure where they had shot from.

"Douche that mountain to my nine o'clock," Slade said.

I rolled the Cobra on the knife edge, feeling better just to be doing something, though Slade didn't know where the gooks were any more than I did. We dropped down the sky like a plummet. I squeezed off a pair of rockets and they arrowed away, leaving wispy crooked little trails of smoke behind, and burst orange in the jungle. I squeezed off another pair. The wet mint of the jungle was swelling in the windscreen at an incredible rate and I pulled out, felt my cheeks sag with the Gs.

Slade was on the radio, telling base we had a bird down.

"Is the crew all right?" I recognized the major's voice on the other end.

"I have not determined that. Request a Medevac."

"Roger the Medevac. What's your time remaining?"

"Three zero minutes plus."

I was over the Loach again. It was wedged between two big ass trees. One of the skids had ripped off and the other was bent out from the ship at a right angle. I couldn't see any movement. They could both be hurt, unable to move, but still alive. At least it hadn't caught fire. Loaches are tough birds, so long as they don't burn. I saw one catch a skid at a hundred knots and tumble end over end and finally stop looking like a lump of scrap metal after the hydraulic press gets through with it, but the pilot walked away. All he got was a broken nose.

"Dustoff estimates a bird your location in four five minutes," the major was saying.

"That's too long," Slade said.

"That's the best they can do. We have another Falcon section on the way up."

"When did it lift off?"

"Five minutes ago."

Slade did not answer. They were really dragging ass down there. They should have had the relief section in the air about twenty seconds after they knew we were coming up here short on fuel. I kept waiting for whoever got Mood to open up on us.

"You see that Lima Zulu to my one o'clock?" Slade asked.

There was a grassy space on the other side of the river. It looked like a picnic area.

"Rog."

"I want you to prep it."

"You're going in after him? That looks like about three hundred fucking meters."

"Somebody's got to."

"O.K. I'll make my runs from the November Whiskey."

So Slade was going to be a hero. Well, I guessed he'd gotten away with it before. There was no way I would have done it. There was no telling who would be down there and there was the time problem because of the fuel. He should have had a company of grunts. We did have a grunt platoon assigned to us for situations like this, called the blue platoon, but it was out on an insertion.

I made a couple of runs on the open space. The rockets didn't cause any secondaries, so it was not mined. Then I turned my copilot loose with the miniguns. They do not sound like any other automatic weapon ever made, do not stutter or chatter, but make a huge shirring noise, like some monster electric appliance. They sound like the biggest Waring blender ever made. The tracer arced down in lazy curves and the ricochets bounced crazily.

"That ought to put their heads down," I said.

"That tat-tat looks nice."

Slade's Huey came across the river and settled into the LZ. I saw his door open and he baled out and another figure jumped out of the back. I thought it was probably Rodriguez, his crew chief. Rod was an old head. He had been here before with the grunts.

They disappeared into the grass. It was a helluva lot higher than picnic grass. Then I saw them again at the edge of the stream, and crossing it, leaning against the current, and they disappeared into the jungle on the other side.

The Huey took off and we circled. I was still sweaty handed and tense. You would think when after a while they had not shot at you it would be possible to relax. I was worried about the fuel too. I flew as gently and smoothly as I could, and beeped the per cent power on down a little with the hand throttle on the collective to save fuel. You are not supposed to do that with a turbine, but we did not fall out of the sky. I decided if Slade was not back in twenty minutes we had to go. I hoped the relief section was coming up balls to the wall. Also, my stomach was knotting and clamping.

We flew around and around and I kept waiting, expecting the shit to start flying any instant, and for all I knew down below was crawling with gooks and they had zapped Slade and Rod and the whole thing was an exercise in futility. I began to be pissed off at Mood. It was not his fault, of course, but I began thinking it was. He was such an eager, useless little dip. In some ways he reminded me of me in the old days and I was not ape over how I had been then and also I just did not like him.

I remember at Christmas during the truce he had been with us just a couple of days and he would sit around listening to us bullshit and you could tell it was killing him not to be able to stick his own crap in, not to have any stories but training stories. Christmas Eve we all got loaded. Somebody had a guitar and we were singing all the songs. Jingle bells, mortar shells, VC in the grass. You can take your merry Christmas and shove it up your ass. Mood was completely in the bag and did not know the words.

Later, after the guitar player was too drunk to pick the chords, I got stuck in the corner with Mood somehow and he got to telling me his life story. I did not want to hear it, but I did not think I could stand up, much less walk away. He came from Minneapolis. He told me he had always liked to play with war toys. That was how shit faced he was. When he was a kid he had lots of Army toys and he used to run convoys. His mother had a rock garden and he made believe that was the Burma Road. One time he got some firecrackers and zapped his own convoy. Most of his toys were metal but he had one half-track made of plastic. He put a cherry bomb in the half-track. It blew the track to hell and a shard of plastic cut his cheek. His mother had been all worried because it almost got his eye and his father told him never to play with firecrackers again. The point of the story was he wanted me to see the scar on his cheek.

We had about five minutes to go on the twenty when the new section got there, a pair of Cobras. The major was really an idiot. There is no way in the world you can carry more than the crew of two in a Cobra, and here we had four people on the ground and two ships low on fuel.

I was about to pack up and head home. There was nothing I could do anyway. Then we saw purple smoke in the grassy space and I made a pass and saw Slade and Rod. Slade was holding a body in his arms. The Huey went back in and they loaded and lifted off.

"Where's the dustoff?" Slade came on the air. He was short of breath, really panting, but he still managed to sound completely calm.

"It never showed," I said. "This is going to be interesting."

"We'll make it."

"You O.K.?"

"Affirm. But Mood's all fucked up. I think his back's broken. They greased the gunner."

"What got 'em?"

"I don't know. There were beaucoup holes in it."

We were barreling back toward the low country. Slade ahead, the three Cobras fanned out behind.

"Has anybody else started looking for Hawkeye?"

"Negative to my knowledge," I said.

"They're probably down there somewhere."

"Rog," I said. "It was probably the same gunner. That gook must be good."

Base came on. "What's your fuel situation?"

"I've had more," Slade said. Presumably the major could read a watch.

"We're diverting the Medevac to my location. You can transfer one three there."

"Where is that guy?" Slade said. "One three is in rough shape."

"Roger. We've been monitoring you. I'm writing you up for the DSC for this."

I thought, if Slade had gotten zapped you'd have made it the Congressional Medal of Honor.

Ahead were the mountains of the Mang Yang. They were deep purple-green again. The cumulus were no longer little fluff clouds, but had swollen into a range of iron gray summits and black valleys. They were almost a reflection of the country underneath them. Each ridge line was lower than the last. We only had to clear a couple more and the Mang Yang and it wouldn't matter if we ran out of fuel or not, there was plenty of open country to auto-rotate down in. We could get down on the road near one of the strongpoints.

Then Slade told base Mood had just died. I pulled

up beside the Huey. I could see into the cargo space and
Rod and one of the gunners were covering Mood with a
poncho. It was flapping in the wind and once it almost
got away from them but finally they got him covered, with
all the corners tucked under.

"That's too bad," the major said. "You did everything
you could. I mean it about the DSC."

We were almost to the Mang Yang when Slade's turbine quit. Turbines don't stop cold, but you just begin to lose power. Slade told what was happening as
calm as ever, but I knew he was in for it and I also
knew I had only minutes or seconds more myself. An
autorotation is no big deal under the right circumstances.
We practice them all the time. But you do need a little
open space or the blades might shear and if they do there
is no telling what might happen. Sometimes the blades
cut right through the cockpit.

"I'm going to try for the cemetery," Slade said.

He was already sinking. The cemetery was the only
possible place. I went past on his side and gave him
thumbs up but he was not looking. I did not have time
to dick around and see what happened. He was sinking
fast, but I still had power and if she held for just a minute or two more I would be all right.

I had a terrible case of the runs. Everyone gets them
from time to time. The Pleiku one-step we used to call
them when we were based down there. Now we call them
the An Khe twist. I made it in to the base all right, although the turbine was beginning to turn down as I

worked into the revetment. I did not even wait for the
blades to quit turning, but jacked open the canopy and
baled out and tooled off for the crapper faster than a
speeding bullet, faster than light.

The major would have been pissed off under other
circumstances. You are supposed to debrief before you
do anything else. But Slade had crashed in the cemetery
and they were trying to recover the dead and wounded
and the major was undoubtedly wondering how he was
going to explain losing two birds in one day. It would not
have been hard if we had gotten a lot of kills. As long
as you have kills the highers never ask questions.

They said Slade almost made it, but he crashed and the
ship tumbled. Rodriguez got thrown free and one of the
door guns got out with some broken bones, but Slade and
the copilot and the other gunner were killed. Maybe
Slade twitched there at the end. He was not the best pilot
I ever knew. Maybe he flared too high and she dropped
out from under him or maybe he let the rpms get too low
trying to stretch the autorotation. Or maybe there was no
way anyone could have made it. Pilots never like to admit
that, though, even to themselves. You always think the
guy did something wrong, and you would have made it.
It is always the other guy who gets it.

After a while I was able to get over to the operations
bunker and debrief and find out what happened and then
I went to see the doc. He gave me some pills and
grounded me. The pills have a lot of opium in them to
help plug you up, but they do not like to have you flying

around half stoned. It was fine by me. I thought I could use a couple of days off.

I went back to the crapper and then to the compound and lay in my room until it got dark. I took a bundle of the pills and they went to work nicely in several ways and I lay looking at my trunk with my name lettered on it, *Chaney, Larry R., WO/2*, and dozing and dreaming. My head was buzzing the way it always does after a full day's flying, a buzz that is a residue of motion and blade flap and turbine whine and radio static, and there were knots in my neck because the helmet weighs so much, and my ears were sore from being cramped and twisted and compressed by the helmet, and I thought about how all those things felt, concentrated on each feeling until it began to wear off. I could not get to sleep and I did not want to eat.

I went over to the bar and got a beer. A couple of people were watching television and there was a poker game going at the corner table. In the old days, when we first came and were a real unit because we had trained together and all come out here together, we would have talked about what had happened, tried to talk it away, but all of the old heads have gone home or gotten greased and there was no one I really wanted to talk about it with. Maybe they were still a unit but I was no longer part of it. As far as I am concerned we are a bunch of pilots who work together, nothing more. That is just as well. We do the job as well as we ever did and at times like this it is easier.

I left the bar without having spoken to anyone and went into Mood's room. I should not have done that. Nobody has door locks and everyone goes in everyone else's room looking for magazines or pornography or liquor to steal, but they get very uptight if you go into someone's room after he has gotten blapped. It is not any respect for the deceased thing, but the Army is very uptight that something might get stolen and the family would complain. That means lots of paperwork and an investigation if what is missing was valuable.

Lying on Mood's bed was a model of a Loach. I had never seen it before. He must have kept it hidden and only worked on it when he was sure he was alone. It was not one of those plastic jobs you glue together and paste decals on, but a real model he had carved out of balsa. It was a nice job. The proportions were perfect and the details, things like the rotorheads, were very realistic. He even had the ADF dome where we put it in our unit. When the Loaches come from Hughes the ADF is on top of the tail boom, but once one of our Loaches had a blade that was not articulating properly and it sliced off the dome and that unbalanced it and then on the next revolution it sliced off the tail boom, so we always modify and put the dome underneath.

I picked it up and saw painted just behind the doors two figures. We paint figures on our ships for kills just the way they do on fighters. Most helicopter pilots have Snoopy complexes. If you stay around any mess in the Nam long enough you will hear us talk about how we wish the other side had choppers so that we could have air

battles and get to be aces. The pilots talk about it jok-
ingly, but I am sure all of us daydream about it. I know
I used to. Mood must have sneaked into his room at lunch,
after Slade and I had dumped on him, and got his model
out of his trunk, or wherever he kept it, and painted the
figures on and then not had time to hide it again before
we left on the afternoon mission. Or maybe he left it out
hoping somebody would come in and see it.

I took the model with me and went into Slade's room.
I was making the rounds. I was sure nobody would miss
Mood's model, although I had no clear idea of why
I wanted it, what I thought I was going to do with it.

Slade's room was very neat. Two pairs of boots under
the bed with the toes so bright they could have been light-
bulbs. Slade was RA all the way. I turned on the bedlamp and lay down on the bed and started through his
magazine pile. Then I got up and went to his cabinet
and found a bottle of Canadian Club that was half full
and lay down again and started working on that. Slade
never drank much himself but he always kept good liquor
around and when you dropped by he would pour you a
shot and maybe have a little one himself. No one ever
stole liquor from him. He had a refrigerator, a small one
of his own, and he kept soda and ginger ale in it. Drinking
with him was very civilized, like having a drink at some
friend's house at home.

I heard them whistling and laughing over in the bar.
Either someone had gotten a new pornographic movie
and they were showing it or else the weather girl was on
the boob tube. The weather girl in Saigon is American

and looks like a Playboy centerfold and every night the troops tune her in and get the weather from Pittsburgh and Denver and Seattle as well as Dong Ha and Cam Ranh and Soc Trang. She is probably responsible for at least four hundred thousand hard ons a day.

Slade had a tape recorder beside his bed. I took another pull at the Canadian Club and plugged the ear piece in and turned the machine on. I thought I would rather listen to Johnny Cash than the troops getting exercised over the weather girl. Slade was a great country music fan. I like the stuff too, and if we were friends it was because of the times I would come into his room for a drink and listen to country and western.

But this was not Johnny Cash or any Grand Ol Opry star, but was a tape to his wife. Lots of people send tapes home instead of letters. This war has done great things for the Japanese tape recorder industry. I have one and I sent a couple of tapes to my father. I thought he would go into town and buy himself a cheap recorder so he could hear them but he wrote me a card that he played them on a machine they let him use at the store. I did not send any more. I did not like the idea of everybody in Tucumcari listening to me.

I almost turned Slade's off, but then I thought it would not make any difference to him and I was never going to meet his wife and I was curious. Most of it was very proper and dull. There was a picture of her and of his two kids on top of the refrigerator and he said he was looking at it as he talked. I had never looked at her closely before. She was a little on the fat side, though you could not tell much about her figure from the picture because she was sitting down. It was taken in their backyard, or somebody's backyard. She was sitting in one of those metal fold-up lawn chairs near a barbecue. She had on a white blouse done up at the neck. It had ruffles down the front.

He talked about the operations we had done recently. It was almost like listening to a debriefing, only he was careful to explain all the technical terms, and to leave out the really shitty things. He talked about Mood, said he was very young but had the right attitude and he thought he would do very well. I hoped he would say something about me, but he did not.

Then near the end he said he hoped she had been thinking about his problem, that she would have to help him make the decision to resign or not. He said the war had not changed much this time and in some ways he thought it was worse than in '64 and '65. He said he thought sometimes that we did not learn anything and there was nothing he could do. We were making many of the same mistakes the French made. He tried to teach his people but that was never enough. But if he got out he did not know what he would do. He said she knew the Army had been good to him and to them and so had the country and they owed it a great deal and he did think he could help. There were always ways you could help, no matter how bad things were. Then he ended up saying he loved her and the children and he would see them soon. With luck he would get there before the tape. Well, he was with the French instead.

I turned off the machine and the bedlamp and had another long pull and lay there. People are such stupid cocksuckers, I thought. All of them. In one way or another. Slade was just as dumb as Mood. He had been around more, that was all. I was going to live through this tour and go home and get out and get me a job flying where I had as little to do with people as possible. I did not want a job with the lines any more. I would fly the mail, someplace like Nevada or maybe out of the country. Me and a twin Comanche or an Aztec full of mail. I would fly at night and turn the cockpit lights down low and there would be nothing but the voices of the engines steady out on the wings and the dials of the instruments and starlight and maybe the moonlight on one wing and I would turn the radios down so low I could not hear the people on the ground, screw air traffic control, or even the bright little dit-dahs of the VOR stations. I would fly and fly and fly through the night, just me and the bird and the sacks of mail, and fuck everything else.

I lay there thinking that way and working on the bottle, and the whiskey and the pills were working inside of me. Finally I got up and picked up Mood's model and went outside. I shut Slade's door carefully and stood there. It was cool. A machine gun was firing out on the green line and an illumination round went off over Hong Kong mountain. Maybe a patrol had run into something up there. The poker game was still on in the bar. Then Major Folsohm came along from the operations bunker and I pulled myself together, held the model behind me.

"One one," he said. "Good evening."

"Yes sir."

"I didn't see you at the mess."

"No sir. I've got dysentery."

He lit a cigarette. I stood there not moving, hoping he could not see the model. I had no idea how I would explain it.

"Doc tells me you've grounded yourself."

"No sir," I said. "Doc grounded me. I'm on the pill."

"Pardon?"

It was all I could do to keep from laughing. "He's giving me those pills with opium in them."

"I see," he said. "We're going to be damn short of pilots after this business today."

There was a long pause. He was waiting for me to say that I was O.K. and would not take any more pills and would go see doc and try to get him to reinstate me on flight status. He wanted me to say I was all hell bent to kill some gooks tomorrow, shits or no. I didn't say anything. There is no way they can make you fly if you are grounded for medical reasons, and he knew it, but he wanted me to pretend I didn't like being grounded. Also, we weren't that short of pilots. I thought he was probably composing some nice lines about my lack of attitude for my next report. That is how they get at you. Or think they do.

In the end I outwaited him and he said, "Well, carry on."

"Yes sir," I said.

I waited until he was in his room and then I dropped Mood's model on the walk. One of the skids snapped off and the model lay there listing to one side and I began to stomp it. The wood cracked and splintered. I stomped it until it was in matchwood size pieces and I ground the pieces into the concrete until they were sawdust.

Then I just stood there for a little, fuzzy headed and breathing hard. A pair of illumination rounds popped off and bathed Hong Kong mountain in yellow-white and the machine gun opened up again firing in too long bursts, as if the gunner was very nervous and could not unlock his finger from the trigger and did not care about burning out his barrel, and the voices in the bar trailed away, and I knew they were all listening, ready to sprint for the bunkers, some of them half pushing their chairs back, but there were no incomings, no faint freight train in the distance rumbling of rockets as they pour through the night, or mortar rounds coming in on a rising whirring like flushing quail and having them fly straight at you with a rising beating of wings, and the talk in the bar started up again. My stomach began to clamp and cramp again. I should not have drunk so much of Slade's whiskey. The last light from the illumination rounds faded down and I headed out behind the compound for the crapper.

A
Walk
in the Rain

RAINING AGAIN. Seems as though it's rained every day since I got here. Forty-one days now. Trenches filled with water, knee deep gumbo everywhere. A major operation to get to the shitter. The bunker concrete sweats, drops of cold water ooze out, collect into puddles on the floors. Everything mildewing. Pair of socks disintegrated this morning as I unrolled them.

My face in the shard of mirror we use to shave with. White as lye. Acne pocks under cheekbones, a few whiteheads on my chin. Thought I would be as dark as black molasses by now — Mother gave me a tube of Sea and Ski when I was home on leave — but same old baby face. My hair looks like straw stubble. Hardly the countenance of a hero.

No chance to be a hero yet (or a coward). No chance to be anything but wet and bored. Which is fine by me. But not really, I do want to see what it's like, what I'll be like.

Would like to get it over with, know about myself one way or the other.

Macklin says maybe tomorrow or the day after we'll send out a long patrol.

More rain. Sandbags at perimeter positions falling apart. Foundations of the tower which holds the fifty cal. machine gun sinking on one side. Tower tilting. Sergeant Edwards spent five minutes cussing out the Seabees who built this place.

Clouds lifted for about an hour at noon and we got a beef drop. C–123 flew over and they pushed out live cattle in parachutes. The troops loved the show, ran out falling and slipping in the mud to round them up. One broke a leg landing. They drove it back to camp bellowing and moaning on three legs and shot it. Fresh steak tonight.

Later a chopper came in with essentials like whiskey. One thing about the Special Forces, we keep as comfortable as possible. Some troops — the Cav and the Marines, for instance — evidently make a fetish of filth, of roughing it.

That would be an easy attitude for us to fall into. We have no contact with the outside world except for air and currently our strip is too muddy to land a plane on. There are twelve Americans here and two hundred strikers, a village with a few platoons of Popular Force troops across the river. The bad guys can wipe us out any time they want to. Our only basis for successful defense is that we can make any attack on us too costly to be worth the price.

But really morale is very good, everything considered. We command, we are responsible for what happens to us in a very direct way.

A new sergeant, Remly, came on the chopper. He knows Edwards and Sergeant Von Kirsten, wants to get in some action. He is going home in two weeks and had spent his whole tour at Nha Trang in supply. Edwards calls him the RAMF — rear area mother fucker — but good-naturedly. Nha Trang does not know he's here. It always amazes me what sharp non-coms can get away with.

Chopper left and clouds dropped back down, filled up the valley like dirty cotton batting.

Well, it's going to happen. Macklin says we send out a long patrol tomorrow and I lead it. I have been on numerous sweeps around the camp, quasi training missions we run to keep from dying of boredom as much as anything else. But this will be the real thing.

We have agent reports that there are two regiments up in the mountains. I asked Macklin if he thought the reports were reliable and he laughed, slapped me on the shoulder. "There ain't no such thing as reliable intelligence in this fucking country."

I am beginning to be nervous. Do not know the troops well enough (or myself?), or the country. Spent an hour studying the maps, trying to etch every feature of terrain, every valley and mountain and stream into my mind. Thank God I have always been O.K. at map reading.

Went outside after dark and the outposts were firing

mortar illumination rounds. They burst in the clouds. Eerie hazy glow, like party lights, like candles shrouded in globes of colored paper.

Tried to sleep late this morning, no success. We push off this afternoon, hold up across the river in the village until 0200, then move into the mountains. We are taking rations for ten days, a tremendous weight. Resupply is too uncertain in this kind of weather to do anything else, though. We have not seen the mountains for more than an hour or two for weeks now.

We are to patrol a series of ridge lines to the northwest. Macklin cautioned me to stay on the high ground where possible. We will try to observe the valleys. Edwards goes with me, fifty of the strikers, commanded by Lieutenant Duong, and a guide. The guide is new, a Chui Hoi, or reformed VC. I am ashamed but do not know all the troops by name yet. They all look so much alike.

Remly wanted to come but Macklin said no. I know what he was thinking: one inexperienced man on a show like this is enough. I shall have to rely heavily on Edwards. Lord only knows how many of these things he's been on — this is his third tour — but I must work at our relationship. Cannot allow myself to appear weak, incompetent. Must solicit and consider his advice, but not rely on him completely.

Nervous half hour packing. I do not want to take too much — those mountains are almost vertical, some of them — but there are so many things I may need. Final list:

rifle, 400 rounds, bayonet knife, smoke and frag grenades, rucksack, plastic bag containing dry socks and morphine, two ponchos and poncho liner, field dressings (we are taking a Vietnamese medic, but I do not trust him for anything serious), Band-Aids, talcum powder, rations, extra cigarettes. I estimate it must all come to around sixty or seventy pounds.

Finished packing and time for lunch. Not hungry. Lay on cot, examined the water stains on the concrete beams of the ceiling. Tightness in my chest and stomach. Mind hopping around. Our call sign is Codfish. Wish they had given us something better, more warlike. Ignominious to be zapped as Codfish six. Corps commander's call sign is Gray Ghost. Colonel Flaherty. He talked to me before I came out here. Said I was going to a good camp. Macklin one of the best, he knew I would do well. Usual crap. Has gray gunfighter's eyes. Coldest eyes of any man I ever saw. Edwards and he were in the Rakkasans, one of the battalions of the 101st Airborne, in Korea together.

At 1800 we formed the men up, inspected them. They were all carrying dozens of grenades. Von Kirsten told Edwards, "Keep away from the little mother fuckers if you get in the shit. If one of them gets hit he'll go up like a fucking ammo dump."

Remly came with us down to the river's edge. Edwards told him to get his RAMF ass back to camp. I think he was hoping Macklin would change his mind at the last minute. He laughed at Edwards, wished us good luck.

Drizzling again. Damn little chance for supporting air

strikes if we get into it. The camp behind us on the bluff very comfortable looking. Tin shelters over the guard positions and the tangled rows of rusting concertina. The leaning tower, the 105mm howitzer with the trailer arms buried in mud, and the duckboard walks. Home sweet home. I suppose really the place looks like a transplant from the Ypres salient.

Riverbank red clay churned to slippery paste. Stream Colorado fast, the water sheeny smooth and dark green except where it broke whitely around the boulders. Bridge here once, but blown long ago by Vietcong sappers, maybe even the Vietminh. Water swirled around one lonesome piling in midstream.

We crossed via sampans. Put equipment in bottoms so we'd have a chance if they capsized. Crews were women, one or two to a boat. They poled us upstream in the calm shore water, then let the current catch the bows.

Into the village on a cobbled road. Houses crowded close on both sides. Naked children playing in the cold mud. Popular Force troops wearing pieces of uniforms, an airborne cap or leopard suit pants. Women in dirty pajamas, conical hats. Pigs, chickens, pariah dogs. Older children followed me, Edwards, shouting, "O.K. Salem, O.K. Salem." Mentholated cigarettes choice items here. Salems number one favorite.

Village chief's compound in the center of the vil. We set up in a schoolroom. He insisted we have tea with him. Wore mottled brown camouflage of ARVN airborne, jump wings, rank of major. Liquid worried eyes and long fin-

gered hands, narrow and graceful. Average life span for a
chief up here about eight months Macklin told me.
Usually they get assassinated, though some get it on operations.

Tried to get some rest, but very nervous. Stupid.
Probably be just a walk in the rain. Also, place crawling
with hungry fleas.

Form the troops at 0130 in the chief's courtyard. Much
tension. Red nubs of cigarettes describing arcs. Match
flare on dark faces. Low voices. Clicks of weapons being
cocked. Radio check with camp. One of the PRC 25s
weak. Probably my imagination. However, I check that
the radio man has plenty of extra batteries.

PFs opened the barbwire gates at the village perimeter.
Moved out along the cobbled road through paddies land.
Gurgle of ditch water. Dog bark breaking the night like
an explosion.

Turned off road onto a trail, start up into the high
country. Rain started too. Trail steep. Pack straps bit
into my shoulders. Five minute rest break every half hour.
Found self checking watch frequently.

Up and up. Throat burned, lungs ached. My radio
man quit, sat down beside the trail, refused to move. We'd
been going only two hours. Edwards, who was up on
point, came back, shouted, "Get up. On your goddamn
feet."

I cringed at the noise, debated reprimanding Edwards
for not observing noise security. We were definitely in

Charlie's country, and no one could say what waited at the next turn in the trail. But the radio man was a more pressing problem.

"Is he hurt?" I asked Binh, the interpreter. "Check his ankles."

"He's done this before, sir," Edwards said. "Get up."

"Binh, tell him to get up," I said.

"He say he can't."

"Tell him we'll give the fucking radio to someone else," Edwards said. "But he's got to get up."

"He say radio very heavy. Numbah ten."

We gave the radio to someone else, arranged for the two of them to take turns. Whole affair consumed fifteen minutes, put us that far behind. I wondered if I shouldn't have called in about it — Macklin told me to call anything I wasn't sure of, anything unusual — but decided not to.

At first light we were nowhere near our first objective. Still raining. Very cold, though we sweated as long as we were moving. Macklin chose the objectives and Edwards said, "The fucking old man was figuring with fucking helicopters."

We climbed to a hilltop, set up. Supreme effort to oversee the setting of the perimeter, placement of automatic weapons, fields of fire, etc. That done I curled up inside my poncho, made it into a tent over me to hold my body heat. Fought to stay awake. Rain pattered on the rubber.

Later Macklin instructed us to move on. He was on the radio himself and I found his voice very reassuring. It was light, of course, but visibility not more than fifty yards. Impossible to place ourselves exactly. If you can't see landmarks, what use are maps? Rain continued, very cold. Edwards said, "Nobody'll ever see us in this crap. Anyway, fucking Charlie ain't stupid. He's somewhere warm and dry."

Rest of morning putting one foot in front of other, thinking no farther ahead than the next leg drive, next foothold, next clump of vines or clump of grass. Either straight up or straight down, it seemed. Each ridge succeeded by a higher one. Hundred A–1 ambush sites. Too wet and cold to sweat them. Visibility stayed zilch. No chance to see into any of the valleys.

Early afternoon. An old French road, completely useless for wheeled or tracked vehicles. Every hundred meters or so it was blown up. We watched carefully for pungi pits and trip wires.

Made bivouac early. Dark by 1630. Troops constructed shelters of ponchos and sticks and vines. Old campaigners masterpieces. Mine held up, but theirs looked hurricane resistant. Edwards and I slept apart. Never do for one mortar round to get us both. Mortar section built Edwards' shelter for him, no one helped with mine. Discrimination.

Miserable night. Could not get warm. Poncho liner soaked, clothes same. Shivered convulsively, arms and legs twitched. I thought we spent some lousy nights in ranger school, but not this bad. Tried thinking of brandy. Hot soup. Then women. Started with one that developed young, in the sixth grade, and worked on through every one I'd ever slept with, or necked with, or even had a letch for, worked diligently to conjure up remembrances of thighs, hair, breasts, taste of sweat, crotch heat, sweet moment of entry. Negative success. Went on to movie stars, but gave that up when I discovered Raquel Welch's breasts were plastic bags filled with dry ice.

Then just lay there, waiting for it to be light, noting guard changes, trying not to look at my watch more than five or six times a minute. Kept telling myself that if the troopies and Edwards could take it, I could too. Not only take it but not let it get to me, had to keep thinking ahead, planning. Sounds like a late late show line, but officers do carry more of a burden. Men can concentrate their energies on shelters, but I am supposed to set up a defense, think what we will do if we get probed, if we get clobbered, etc. Well, as they kept telling us in jump school, don't bitch, you volunteered for this. Only out here there is no way to unvolunteer, to quit the program.

Today same as yesterday. Colder if possible. I'd like to have along some of those reporters who always picture this country as a steamy jungle.

A lot of pungi pits. A rusty old French mine. It was in the middle of the road, dirt washed away from it, almost rusted through. Point element dug around it before I got there. We thought of bringing it in, but it was too heavy, an anti-vehicle mine, so we threw it over the edge of the road. This country is full of minefields. The French didn't keep very good track of theirs, and of course Charles isn't about to tell us where his are.

Slept with my radio man, the one who quit. Carried the radio fine today, without being spelled. Edwards says he probably hoped we'd turn around and go back in, but now that he knows we won't he's fine. He built my shelter so that it blocked off most of the wind. All the troops smell like fish and nuc bam, the sauce they pour on everything, but I guess that is one of the prices of acceptance. I was certainly warmer and managed to sleep a little.

Rain and cold again. Stayed up on a trail along a ridge line most of the day. My feet blistering badly. I tried to change my socks at least once a day, but it didn't do any good, they were all wet. Hands and feet very white, wrinkled, as if I'd been washing dishes or swimming too long.

Moving generally west, closer to Laos. Border four or five kilometers. Not that this particular border means anything. Edwards, who spent six months in Laos in '64, says the only time the Laotians fight, our Laotians anyhow, is when they think their opium trade is in danger. We have a great bunch of allies in this war.

Which brings up the point of why we bother to fight it. People out here never talk about that, though many must think about it. The professionals would tell you it's only a job, like any other, and I suppose the draftees just want to live through it. Certainly nobody believes we are doing this to help another democracy. From what I've seen and heard, if this country and its government are typical of Asian democracies, you can't blame the people for wanting something else.

And me? Why me? Excellent question. I went in because I didn't feel strongly enough to stay out. And once

I was in I figured I might as well do it right. I suppose, basically, I'm just carried along by the system. So are most people, I guess. If I make it through I won't regret having done it, I'm pretty sure of that.

Rain so cold today I thought it would turn to sleet. Fingers stiff, hard to write. Lots of pungi pits. Hillsides, where they are open, spiked with anti-helicopter poles. One trail used recently. Bunkers along it every few hundred meters where they can take cover from air and arty.

Binh says all troops want to go in. Good. So do I. But what I can do about it I don't know. Edwards a hard one. Talking to camp this evening, and Von Kirsten asked what it was like out here. "Good clean fun," Edwards said.

Later told me he thinks we'll hit something soon. He's sure they're around. Which makes sense. It's a cinch the good fairy didn't dig those pits or set the anti-chopper poles.

Fatigue, rain, cold, getting to us. Packs lighter as we eat through rations, but you don't notice it. Have to keep after the troops constantly to maintain spacing, rear security. Duong not much help. They don't pay much attention to him, or perhaps he does not relay my orders accurately.

Edwards caught two soldiers trying to get rid of some of their grenades. As mentioned, they are all carrying enough grenades to fight several pitched battles. Don't have much faith in their marksmanship. The ones I've seen work out on the range no threat to Olympic records. Edwards had Binh tell them that we know how many gre-

nades were issued (a lie) and if any are missing when we
get back they'll all have their pay docked.

A contact this morning. Just a sniper, but at least I can
say I've been under fire.

We were starting down a mountainside to cross a valley,
get up on another ridge line, and someone opened up on
us. Fired five or six rounds, no damage. Edwards said it
was probably a sentry firing warning shots, but one hit off
in some rocks to my left, made a whining ricochet sound.

Guide giving trouble. We must be near something, because he is obviously on edge. Every time we leave high
ground he goes to the rear of the column, and is very vague
about where we are. Up to now he has been excellent at
showing our positions, which has been handy, as map
reading so hard with every prominent landmark obscured
by fog and clouds.

Duong less than eager too. Told me his feet are too sore
to go on twice today. I made a point of showing him my
blisters during a break, but still he complains. And these
are supposed to be hot rod troops by Vietnamese standards.
In the Forces Americans command. It must be a real ball
when all you can do is suggest things.

We crossed over into Laos today. Still too foggy for
much observation.

A note about the country. It has a certain lonely
beauty. I am wet and cold and generally uncomfortable,
but even in this condition I have to admit the country is
impressive. We've seen at least five waterfalls that must

be among the most lovely in the world. Rich French-
men used to come up here before the war on tiger safaris.
Whenever the fog lifts, as it does once or twice a day, you
have a sense of size, of great distances, of emptiness. The
French called campaigning up here the war of the vast
empty spaces. Since the village we have seen no signs of
humans except for the road, the mine, the pungis, the
shots.

Another contact this morning. Almost blew cool. I have
been in the Army fourteen months now, in training for
this moment most of the time. I got through jump school
and ranger school and unconventional warfare school, all
of it aimed to train me to react properly in a situation
like this morning, and I almost broke and ran.

Was up on point going across another valley. Edwards
and I alternate on point. We are not supposed to separate,
a standing rule, but everyone breaks it. You have to to be
effective.

They opened up on us from the opposite hillside, an
automatic weapon — I think it was a BAR — and some
rifle fire. I got down behind some rocks and the second
volley came in, ricochets whining all around, and nasty
little flat cracks as a few went by close overhead.

I yelled for my trusty troops to fan out and move forward (fix the enemy, get some idea of his strength) and
stood up myself. They were all running back up the hill.
I got back down and watched them. Some more fire came
in, very near to me. I can't tell you how alone I felt. The
troops were back in the edge of the jungle, under cover,

and I was sure I was going to be hit. It was the hardest thing I ever did in my life not to follow them, not to sprint after them.

Then Edwards got the mortar going and dropped five rounds on the other slope and the firing quit. He came down the hill with another squad and we crossed and found where they had been firing from, behind some rocks and a bamboo stand. They had been cutting pungis. The ground was littered with them, sharp whittled stakes maybe a foot long. There were some bundles tied with strings. It was probably a squad or less.

"We surprised us a fucking pungi factory," Edwards said on the radio.

At first, when I got over shaking, I felt kind of good. I had not run. I kept waiting for Edwards to say something congratulatory, but he didn't. Then I began thinking about it and felt less good. My troops broke and ran, which is always the officer's fault, and only God and I know how close I came to running with them.

My radio man, who was one of those who bugged out, built my shelter again. If he's aware that he did anything wrong, and of course he is, he does not show it. Duong has not mentioned what happened.

Macklin ordered us to start back in tomorrow.

Moved incredibly fast and hard today. Everyone knows we are going in. No one complained. Everyone was eager to go at the end of each rest break. Even the security was better. Both Duong and the guide know exactly where we are, keep suggesting shortcuts. I must admit I am tempted to take them, cut off several miles of walking, but the route Macklin worked out has fewer potential ambush sites. Coming home is when they ambush you.

These people remind me of an old horse we had. It had a helluva hard mouth and plenty of will power. You could switch it and spur it and shout and it went pretty much where it wanted at its own pace. But when it knew it was headed for the barn there was no stopping it.

My blisters worse. Socks blood stained.

Still brooding about yesterday, over what I might have done differently, better. It is a question of intangibles, I think. If I had had more presence, more experience, if the men had known me better and had confidence in me, maybe they wouldn't have split. On the other hand maybe they would have. What would have happened to me if Edwards hadn't been in control up above, got the mortar going? Or if the guys across the valley had been a company looking for a fight rather than a work detail? It would have been damn bad for my health, that's what.

Talked to Edwards, he says we ought to put whole squad in the cage. Have not confessed how close I came to running myself. Could make a joke of it, but he would see through it.

Macklin told us he has sent another patrol southwest of camp. I imagine Remly's on that one. I'd like to compare notes if and when we both get back.

Another blistering march. Near end of string physically. Still raining, still cold. Camp tomorrow.

I do not understand these people, how they think. They have been at war for how long now — more than a decade — and you'd think they want to get it over with, see that the way to get it done is to find the enemy (what this patrol is ostensibly all about) and kill him. If we don't kill him out here, he'll come to us, to their homes, which will be even more unpleasant. The hard way is the easy way, in the long run.

They do not see it like that. All they want to do is get back to camp (hardly the acme of luxury, even by local standards). So do I, of course, but not in the same way. Charlie does not operate like this or the war would have been over years ago. Would never have started.

They are amazing physical specimens, though. I was an all-conference forward twice, went through jump and ranger school with less trouble than most, and a bunch of five-foot-two hundred and twenty pounders are walking me to death. Edwards does not look any too well either, which is a small consolation.

This A.M. foggiest yet. Felt as though every time I moved an arm or leg I was slicing through some medium the viscosity of water. Morning cookfires like rubies floating in the mist.

Couldn't hold them back. Terrific rate of march. Came out of mountains, hit valley about six clicks above camp. Paddies, some under cultivation. First signs of civilization. Old men and women and boys working. Water buffaloes, shaggy haired and thick horned and caked with mud to their bellies. Boys ride them, prod them with sticks. Houses and bamboo huts, all deserted. People pull back into the village at night.

Troops practically ran. No hope of maintaining spacing, security. Everyone slung his weapon. Marched along cobbled road beside old railroad bed. Ties overgrown with weeds. Every hundred meters or so a rail ripped up, heated, curled into weird and fanciful shapes. Modern sculpture.

Feet hurt like hell. Blisters squishing each step. Troops laughing and happy. I had an ailment even worse than sore feet — tip of my penis raw from chafing against we coarse cloth and zipper of tiger suit. Nobody here wears underclothes. They rot, give you jungle rot. Chafing caused me to sidle along crabwise.

Through the vil. Kids ran along asking for Salems. Edwards told Binh to tell troops not to steal chickens. PFs looked very comfortable and fat, garrison troopish. Our heroes sneered at them.

On the riverbank we spread out, lay down, waited for sampans. Edwards offered me his canteen. Contents tasted like warm cherry soda. Very cloying. I drank dutifully while he watched.

"Fizzies," he said. "I always carry fucking Fizzies for special occasions."

Camp seemed like epitome of comfort, civilization. Showered, changed clothes, shaved. Medic worked on my blisters, offered to put iodine on my dick. This affliction evidently fairly common. Medic told me of one man who died when a leech crawled up his penis.

We debriefed. Gave Macklin all details we left out of radio transmissions. When we told him about troops running, he nodded. No comment. I do not know what he really thinks.

Mess tent. Cold beer by six pack. Definite feeling of cameraderie. All the sergeants gathered around, Edwards and I (mainly me) on talking jags. Retold every minute of the operation with suitable embellishments. I noticed Von Kirsten and Seegar, another of those sergeants with twenty years and three wars, sitting at the end of the table grinning slightly ironical but friendly grins, watching us but not really with us, enjoying our stories but not really denigrating them — giving us the old campaigner's seal of approval. I admit I welcomed it.

Huge lunch. Canned peaches by the pound. Water no problem out there, but I was very dehydrated. Definitely tight from beer.

Then Macklin came into the tent, told us the other patrol was in trouble, had been ambushed. My first thought uncharitable: why the hell does this have to happen now, just when I'm relaxing?

Hurried down to commo bunker. Picture came in in choppy little snatches, like pieces of a puzzle. Remly hit in thigh, may have gotten it in femoral artery, bleeding badly. Sporadic sniper fire.

We requested a Medevac, got out plot board, began to work the 105. The patrol only five clicks out from camp, within easy range. I stood in bunker door, called corrections, and the gun fired right over my head, skull splitting crack, muzzle blast a slap in the face.

We fired fifteen rounds and the bad guys broke contact.

Ten minutes later the Medevac chopper flew directly over camp, an H–34 with red crosses behind the doors. Usually they send gunbirds along as escorts, but this one all alone. They loaded Remly on and we heard the bird chopping through the clouds but did not see it again.

Back to mess tent, picked up where we left off. Another can of peaches. I thought of Remly, imagined the Medevac, Remly's face chalky and the eyes big pupiled and far away from the morphine and the blood seeping through the dressing. The long jolting ride to Danang, the wind icy, landing on a pad outside the operating room and the stretcher bearers lifting him out gently and hurrying him into the white room with the white masked doctors and attendants and the glare of fluorescent lights, peeling back the field dressing from hamburgered flesh. Only person who mentioned him aloud was Edwards, who muttered, half to himself, "Wanted action. Shit."

Many beers later, after we had discussed our patrol out of reality, made it into a wild comedy with only the barest relation to actual events, after we were thick tongued and slurring words and empty cans were stacked high in front of us and I had forgotten my feet except when I stood to get another beer or take a piss, Macklin came in smiling, sat down with us, said Remly will be O.K., bullet missed both the artery and the bones, and we all laughed drunkenly, but with relief, and Edwards said in his inimitable fashion, "The dumb fuck. An easy Purple Heart."

Situation normal again. Rained about an inch last night.

The squad that bugged out has been put in cages, four by six barbwire boxes. Major Minh, the Vietnamese camp commander, actually went on about shooting one as an example. Macklin heard him out quietly, said the cage would be fine. So now all eight of them are out in the wet and everyone who goes by says something to them, or at least throws them a dirty look.

I keep away from that part of camp. What would have happened to me if I'd bugged out? Nothing, or something a lot worse than spending a day in a barbwire dog house.

And the patrol. What did we accomplish? Killed no enemy, no friendly casualties either. Standoff. We covered a lot of ground, but didn't really see anything. There could be five Chinese corps in those valleys.

As for me, I still don't know if I can hack it or not in a real show. Maybe no one knows, and the best you can do is take each situation as it comes. If I stay around here long enough I will certainly have enough chances. We go on a routine sweep tomorrow and Macklin says that two or three days after he wants me to go into the mountains again. There is a valley about six kilometers inside Laos we are to check out. It will be a show much like this last one — if I allow myself to think about it I will start to get nervous, which is foolish. It will probably be just another walk in the rain.

The
Last
Operation

IT SHOULD HAVE BEEN ONE OF Anson's last operations. He was doing a book, for which he had received and spent an advance from an American publisher, and he figured he needed only three more stories to finish it. He wanted something on the Koreans, his section on the Special Forces wasn't complete, and he wanted to ride one of the new air-cushion boats, the PACVs, that they were testing down in the Delta, and then he was going back to England, he'd even bought his plane ticket. He was hoping for some sort of part-time assignment with TIME-LIFE, but said he was going home whether it came through or not.

He asked me if I wanted to go along for the Koreans, and I said sure. Since he was shooting strictly for his book, we wouldn't be in competition, and I always liked traveling with him. He had planned to go out with the Capitol Division, but I had already done that, and suggested we do the Marines. It didn't make any difference to him, one Korean was as good as another, and we went down to JUSPAO and booked ourselves. That was Tuesday morning.

We left Saigon on Wednesday, took flight 653 up to Danang, spent the evening in the Press Center bar drinking vodka collinses, and flew down to Chu Lai the next morning on a US Marine O–47. Captain Kim, the Korean Marine PI officer, met us there, and drove us by jeep to brigade headquarters.

The headquarters was situated on a hill overlooking a small landing zone, and was very sharp and permanent looking. A neat row of saplings had been planted on each side of the main approach road, boardwalks connected the main buildings, and sandbag and gravel paths bordered by 105mm shell casings went to the others. All the buildings were solidly constructed, with carefully fitted joints and camouflage paint jobs and screens that weren't torn or saggy. The brigadier's house had a hot water heater and an air conditioner, as well as a precisely clipped little lawn of Kentucky bluegrass out in front. There were many sentries, in faded starched fatigues, carrying M2s, and they snapped salutes and shouted something at you in Korean every time you came within fifty feet. But outside all the doors were deep sandbagged bunkers, reminders that this was still a war zone, even if a well policed one. Kim told us that the VC had mortared them twice. The Koreans had been shifted up from II Corps only a month before, and had had three big fights the first week.

We dropped our gear in a barracks for transient VIPs and field grade officers. The building was made of plywood and corrugated tin roofing over a framework of three by fives, with lots of screen for ventilation. The cots had clean sheets on them, there were thong shower slippers beside every bed, and each of us had an enlisted orderly. Besides Anson and myself, there were two Korean lieutenant colonels staying there. Carefully laundered extra uniforms — tiger camouflage suits and jungle fatigues — hung above their cots from the mosquito netting wire.

The captain left us alone to wash up before lunch. Anson lay down on his cot and stretched, his arms behind his head.

"Rather splendid, this," he said.

"The comforts of home," I agreed.

One of the orderlies came up from the other end of the barracks and made a little bow. I bowed back.

"Latrine shower," he said. "I show, you come?"

We followed him outside. The latrine was a magnificent four seater. They had it faced so that you could look out across a valley to a big landing zone, where every few minutes an H–34 or a Huey clattered in or out. In the washroom the orderly filled plastic bowls for us and we sloshed water over our faces and combed our hair. The scars on Anson's face seemed rawer, redder, when they were wet.

By then it was 1300, so we went up to the senior officers' mess. Adjacent to the dining room was a varnished wood bar and lounge with comfortable wicker chairs. Pictures of dress parades and portraits of officers and plaques hung on the walls. Everybody was there waiting for us, the general and the chief of staff and about fifteen lieutenant colonels and majors. We were introduced to all of them, but the only two I really remembered were the general and the colonel. The brigadier had the kind of beard that always makes a man look as if he's been in the field over-night, two large black moles on the left cheek, a thick ridge of scar tissue over his eyebrows, and did not talk so much as grunt. Except for the immaculate uniform, he re-minded me of a Hollywood Chinese bandit chief. The colonel's face was well fleshed and sleek, and his hair was neatly combed and glossy. He had very small, very black eyes, that moved over us quickly but thoroughly. All of them were big shouldered and hard-looking.

Lunch was a little strained. We sat at the head of the table, Anson on the general's right and me on the colonel's left. Anson told some funny stories, and I thought most of them spoke enough English to understand, but I couldn't be sure. He told the one about the Chinese nymphoma-niac in Singapore, and I was a little worried that being Asians they might not appreciate it, but the general laughed.

"You English, yes?" he asked.

"Yes sir," Anson said.

"You know Colonel Brinkley-Davis? Maybe now gen-eral?"

"Brinkley-Davis? No sir, I can't say that I do."

"In Korean War I liaison to Gluckshires."

"I say," Anson said politely.

"Every morning staff meeting in Colonel Brinkley-Davis tent. Drink tea, not coffee. With Americans always cof-fee."

"Barbaric beverage, coffee," Anson said. "But I've come to the point where I must have it to start the day. His influence." He nodded at me.

"Have you been in Vietnam long, Mr. Bender?" the colonel asked.

"About three months."

"And Mr. Anson?"

"Twenty-three months," Anson said. "I have been on fifty-seven operations."

He was very proud of that number. Also that he had been wounded three times, more than any other correspondent.

"For whom do you work?" The colonel spoke English very formally, but almost without accent.

"Free lance, sir," Anson said. "We're both free-lancers, but I have TIME-LIFE accreditation."

The general spoke to the colonel in Korean. "The general would like to know if there are any reporters in Vietnam for PLAYBOY," the colonel said.

"Not that I know of," I said.

"Does the general like PLAYBOY?" Anson asked.

"Number two," the general said. "Very good, but nudist magazine number one. Two year ago I go Camp Pendleton, buy many nudist magazine. You know Camp Pendleton?"

"Yes," I said. "A little."

"Very many nudist magazine," the general said.

After lunch we followed the colonel to his office for a briefing. The colonel walked with a major, and Anson and I were some way behind.

"The general's rather kinky, isn't he?" Anson said. "They're all rather kinky."

"They're fine," I said.

The briefing was smooth, well organized and well presented. The colonel was very good. He stood in front of the big map, his pants razor creased and bloused and just properly faded, his boots as gleamy as his hair, and drew graceful arcs and circles with the pointer, and occasionally rapped it on the floor to emphasize something. He also used a quick chopping taequando gesture. Kim sat in an office chair at the back of the room, a looseleaf notebook across his lap, and, whenever the colonel couldn't remember a statistic, the captain supplied it. They even gave out realistic figures for their own casualties, which surprised me. My last operation had been with a famous American regular infantry division, whose PI officers were habitual liars, and it was nice when people came clean.

We asked a few questions, and left with Kim. He asked us what we wanted to do, and we said we wanted some pictures of civic action — medical teams and rice harvesting, that sort of thing — and some of combat.

"Civic action too far drive today," Kim said. "Tomorrow we go."

"O.K.," I said.

"What about combat?"

"Contact very light."

"We don't need much," Anson said. "Just some pictures in the field."

"Can be arranged."

"Splendid," Anson said.

"Will there be any taequando practice here?" I asked.

"Taequando team practice 1730 hours. Will be honored if you observe."

He said he'd come by for us, and we thanked him. We went to our quarters. Neither of the lieutenant colonels was there. Anson unlaced his boots and lay down. I got a book out of my pack — Jones's *The Thin Red Line* — and stretched out myself, and began to read.

After a while Anson started to snore, and I put the book down and looked at him. He seemed very young. He was actually twenty-five, but he looked about seventeen. He wore his hair long and scruffy at the nape of his neck and over the ears, English schoolboy style, and, except for the scars, his face was smooth and soft. The worst scar was in the cleft of his chin, and he had another bad one under his left ear. Both of those were from the time he was on the Coast Guard cutter that was accidentally strafed by a section of F–4s. They made nine passes, with rockets and 20mm cannon, and killed or wounded everybody on the ship. The captain had been up on the bridge trying to signal them away with an aldis lamp when a five-inch rocket blew his head off. Anson's chin had been split by a fragment from a 20mm cannon shell, and, if you looked at him closely head-on, one side of his jaw was slightly higher than the other. Also, his chest was badly burned. Without a shirt on he looked as if you had stuck him in about thirty places with a glowing cigar tip. Sometimes he got the shakes in his sleep and trembled himself awake, but now he was peaceful.

Our two orderlies saw that I wasn't reading or sleeping. They smiled and I motioned them to come down. They were in skivvies and T-shirts, and, while they weren't tall, maybe five-six and five-eight, their legs and shoulders were extraordinarily well developed. They sat down on the cot across from me, grinning. One, the smaller, had huge teeth that were very white and bucked, so that when he smiled he achieved a Charlie Chan effect. The other was more stolid.

"Me Lim," Charlie pointed to himself, then to the other. "Him Pak."

"Jim Bender," I said.

"Mr. Bendow," Pak said.

"You are American?" Lim asked.

"Yes."

"And you friend?"

"English."

"Engrish," Lim repeated. "Lichard Burton."

"Yes," I said. "Same-same Richard Burton. You like Richard Burton?"

"Numbah one. Lizabeth Taylow, Cleopata, numbah one also."

"She used to be number one," I said. "Now number ten. Fat."

Lim laughed and shook his head. "Numbah one."

We talked about movies for quite a while. Lim was an avid fan. Humphly Bogup was one of his great favorites. Pak liked John Wayne.

"Talk about singers," Anson said, without opening his

eyes. I don't know how long he had been awake. "Enough bloody cinema."

"Singers?" Lim asked.

I strummed an imaginary guitar.

"Ah," he said. "Beatle. Beatle numbah one."

"Number two," Anson said. He sat up. "Rolling Stones number one. You know Rolling Stones?"

Lim jumped up, shut his eyes, and began to do the jerk.

"Yes, yes," Anson said. "Very good. Splendid."

Lim sat down. "You know Pat Boom?"

Anson nodded.

"What numbah?"

"Number one thousand," Anson said. "Number twelve thousand."

We all laughed. Lim started to say something, but Pak jabbed him in the ribs, and they both snapped to attention. Captain Kim came in, returned their salute, and sat down.

"All is satisfactory?"

"We couldn't be better," I said.

He nodded to Lim and Pak and they went back to their end of the room. We put on our boots.

The taequando team worked out on the small LZ below the operations building. The members wore loose white judo suits, and all of them wore black belts. We had our cameras and moved around, shooting busily. First they went through a series of warm-up exercises in perfect unison, whirling and thrusting and chopping and kicking and shouting exactly together, then broke up into pairs and sparred, pulling the thrusts and kicks. The real spectacle, the breakage exhibition, came last. You've probably seen pictures of that, ours or someone else's. They lined up in one long row and each man broke a brick over his forehead; they chopped through piles of four bricks with the edges of their hands; and, as a grand finale, one man split six bricks. We took some portraits and were introduced to the six-brick man. The edge of his hand felt like a horse's hoof.

On the way back to our quarters Kim asked, "Was satisfactory?"

"Very," I said.

"It was superb," Anson said.

"Taequando is a form of karate?" I asked.

"Yes, nearly same karate."

"Some judo also, isn't there?" Anson asked.

"Mostly same karate."

"How about the bricks," I said. "Doesn't it give them a headache when they break bricks like that?"

"Head very hard," Kim said. "Many years practice. No headache."

We washed and went to the mess and had a few beers before dinner. The general and the colonel came in together and we all stood up. The general was hungry, so we went straight into the dining room. Anson's and my seating cards had been reversed. I guess they thought I'd lose face if I had to sit by the colonel all the time. Before they brought the food, the chaplain, a major, said a long prayer. It was in Korean, so of course I didn't understand any of it, but I heard the words Viet Cong about four

times. Later Kim gave us a poop sheet on the general,
which said he had gotten religion, Catholicism, just after
the landing at Inchon, and then wiped out a whole North
Korean regiment with one company, or something.

After dinner we went back to quarters with the lieutenant colonels. One of them produced an unopened bottle
of Johnny Walker black label, and we drank to the ROK
Marines, the US Marines (the Koreans always referred
to our Marines as brothers), the Press Corps, and killing
VC.

In the morning Kim came by for us with his jeep. We
got on the Quang Ngai road and drove for maybe five
kilometers. There was a lot of traffic, six by sixes filled
with typically sloppy ARVNs, who shouted at us and
whistled and laughed, cyclos, three-wheeled Lambretta
buses, peasants and bicyclists using the shoulders, and a
US Marine convoy. At the head of the convoy were an
M–48 tank and an Ontos, the antitank weapon with six
106mm recoilless rifles, and a couple of APCs, then about
a mile of trucks, bumper to bumper, with another Ontos
at the end. Some of the trucks had .50cal MGs mounted
on the roofs of the cabs, and the men all wore battle
dress, helmets and heavy flak jackets. The vehicles were
filmed with a fine white dust, and the drivers and gunners
were red-eyed and hot. The Koreans had strung double
rolls of concertina on both sides of the road, and, across
the wire, the farmers were slogging through the muck
of the paddies harvesting. They looked small and tired
and dirty, sullen and worn down, and their movements
were hypnotically deliberate.

We went through two villages, and turned into a yard in front of a house with a red cross over the door. A bench outside was lined with Vietnamese; pregnant women, a man whose right leg was a withered stump that ended below the knee, and mothers and children. Inside a Korean doctor and two medics were working. They wore white knee length dusters, and the doctor had a mirror reflector on his head. He was looking at an infected ear and the medics were swabbing with an awful smelling purple goo the shaved head of a little girl who had ringworm. We took a roll apiece and then talked to the doctor. He had graduated from Johns Hopkins and was very hip on sanitation. Sanitation was a worse problem than the VC, these people were filthy and didn't know any better. He wanted to know if either of us came from Baltimore, and seemed disappointed when we said we didn't. He said that next to Seoul, Baltimore was his favorite city.

We got back in the jeep and drove on through another village. A few hundred yards beyond was the turnoff to the Second Battalion bivouac. The intersection was guarded by two sandbagged emplacements, one holding a .30cal machine gun and the other a BAR. Across the road was a long sweep of rice paddies, patched with bamboo thickets, and bordered by a distant treeline. Working in the nearest paddy, side by side with the peasants, were six Koreans in skivvy shorts and canary yellow undershirts with red borders and ROK across the chests.

"This is great," I said.

"It's a pity we don't have color," Anson said.

We slung our cameras around our necks and started toward the paddy. Kim stayed in the jeep, in the shade of the cloth top.

"I can see it now," I said. "The sword and the sickle. Two full pages in LIFE domestic. Koreans kill Cong bare-handed. Toil side by side with peasants. Also bare-handed. Builds bare-handed understanding."

We worked hard for forty-five minutes. We took group shots from the dikes, then climbed down in the muck and took portraits and group shots with wide-angle lenses. We went around ahead of the harvesters, and for a while Anson was down on his knees so that he could shoot from the level of the sickles. We got them bundling the rice and carrying it over their shoulders along the dike and through a break in the barbwire and across the road and up a small hill behind the emplacements, where several teams of Koreans and peasants were pumping two foot-operated threshers. Our boots were soaked and covered with ooze, and Anson's pants were slimy wet to his thighs.

After a cigarette break, we shot the threshing. Symbolic shots of Korean and Vietnamese legs (the Korean legs were invariably about three times the diameter of the Vietnamese) driving the pedal up and down, pictures of men applying the heads of bundles of rice to the threshing wheel, etc. We even got down on the ground in the grain to get the sweating faces over the spill of rice coming off the wheel. By the time we quit I was oily with sweat and my hair was full of chaff and I itched everywhere. I took off my shirt and shook it out and tried to comb the chaff out.

Kim had his driver open some rations. I had a pack of

blue heat tablets, so we had warm lunch and heated some coffee afterward. Kim wanted to know if we'd like to go on to Quang Ngai and take some pictures of a taequando expert teaching a class of Vietnamese high school girls.

"I say," Anson said. "High school girls. Do they break bricks?"

"Not yet. Many years practice required break bricks."

"Pity that," Anson said. "Bricks make number one photos."

"You do not wish to proceed?"

"Sure," I said. I had had a good day's work and would just as soon have gone back, but did not want to offend him. "It sounds very interesting."

Quang Ngai was about twelve clicks farther on. It was the headquarters for ARVN 2nd Division, so, as we went along, there were more ARVNs and fewer Koreans. In the villages were quite a few Popular Force troops, dressed in black pajamas or odd combinations of parts of uniforms. They carried carbines or M1s, but the M1s were too big for them, made them look like dirty and rather malicious children playing with cannons.

We got to the city about 1700, but found that taequando wouldn't begin until 1800. Neither of us were happy about that, because it meant we'd have to drive back at dusk and in the dark, but Kim didn't seem worried.

"Area is secure," he said.

He had some people to see, so Anson and I went in a bar and had a few beers. We got to the high school just before 1800. The instructor looked like another six-brick man, but the girls were tiny, reed-armed, and hidden in multiple folds of their judo suits. They went through an abbreviated warm-up routine, and their shouts often came out as squeals and giggles. We shot a lot of film, but the lighting was poor and I wasn't hopeful of getting much.

I was nervous all the way back. While it was light I kept scanning the treelines and canebrakes, and, after it was dark, I imagined every shape and shadow was a VC with a Chicom. Anson had scrambled into the back, which meant he was worried about road mines. He was more afraid of mines than anything else, and had a theory that if you were in the rear seat you might be blown free. Nothing happened, though, and we got back in time for a late meal.

Afterward we had a few drinks with the lieutenant colonels again, and Anson was very gay and funny, the way he always was after pressure. He told many stories, about the US Marine landing at Chu Lai where the troops came storming out of the amtracks and up the beach like John Wayne in *The Sands of Iwo Jima* only to find twenty photographers on the top of the first dune taking pictures of it all, and the time he was out with a Regional Force group in sampans and the bowman in his sampan fished during a firefight and caught a five-foot snake right in the worst of it, and many others. Finally we turned in, but I did not sleep well. It was a windless night, hot and stuffy beneath the mosquito netting. My sheets became knotted and sweat-damp, and my skin felt grimy and oily. Three or four times the horizon glowed yellow from a flare. Twice I got up for a drink of water, and both times there was a red nub of cigarette glow under Anson's netting.

Anson shook me just after dawn. Captain Kim was standing beside him. I pushed the netting back and sat up and groped with my feet for the thongs. My mouth was filled with a thick stale dry taste.

"What gives?" I asked.

"I beg pardon," Kim said. "But very big contact. Many many VC."

"They tried to overrun a company," Anson said. "The colonel's going out to inspect the battlefield. They'll allow us along too."

I washed quickly, and got back into my jungle fatigues. They were the only clothes I'd brought with me from Danang, because I'd expected to be in the field, or at least in tents, and now, after two days, they were pretty high. We packed our rucksacks and carried them and the camera bags up to the mess hall. The waiters brought out hot coffee. We were the only people there.

"Where's the colonel?" I asked.

"Eat already," Kim said. "Now briefing."

The waiter brought plates of scrambled eggs and bacon, and a plastic wicker basket filled with hard rolls. I made myself eat half the eggs and bacon, but Anson did not touch anything. He smoked two cigarettes and sipped his coffee. He was obviously nervous, and making no attempt to hide it. He was always like that before he went into the field, but you couldn't blame him, not after that cutter incident. I wasn't worried myself, because I didn't think a bird colonel, even this one, would be going any place very dangerous.

"How many dead?" I asked Kim.

"Ten Korean KIA. Thirty VC. But that only within perimeter. Have not yet searched outside perimeter."

"Any prisoners?"

He shook his head. Anson excused himself and went outside.

"Mr. Anson is not well?" Kim asked.

"Nervous," I said. "He'll be all right." I mouthed another forkload of eggs.

"You are writer as well as photographer?" Kim asked.

"I write captions sometimes."

"Who is greatest English writer?"

"Christ, I don't know. Shakespeare, I guess."

"William Shakespeare," he said. "I have read many plays of Shakespeare. *Othello, King Lear, Hamlet.*"

"Which one did you like best?"

"*King Lear.* Is very beautiful."

"Not *Hamlet*? Most people like *Hamlet* best."

"No," he said. "I find character of Hamlet is too very complex. Also I read the works of Erskine Caldwell."

Anson came back in and sat down. He drummed his fingers on the tabletop.

"The captain reads Shakespeare and Erskine Caldwell," I said.

"Fancy that," Anson said.

"Shakespeare is superior," Kim said.

A lieutenant came in and saluted Kim. They talked in Korean, then Kim said, "We must go LZ."

Kim and the lieutenant insisted on carrying our gear. We walked to the LZ where the taequando team had practiced. An H–34 was there, and the Koreans threw our

stuff on board, shook hands with us, and left. The ship
looked old and rickety. There were a couple of patches on
the skin just aft of midships and the area behind the ex-
hausts was scorched black and the nose had oil smears. I
did not like H–34s to start with: they shook and bucked
and clattered much more than Hueys, and reminded me of
a car I'd owned when I was a kid, an old $150 Pontiac that
was always dropping its driveshaft.

Anson had flown with one of the pilots before and they
stood off to one side chatting, while I talked to the door
gunners. One was a tall thin kid with bad acne and a
ragged blond mustache. The other was equally tall and
skinny, but a Negro. The colonel and his bodyguard, an
enormously broad man who carried an M2 with folding
stock, two forty-fives, and strangling gear, came out of
the operations building and started down the hill to the
LZ. The pilots and gunners came to attention and saluted,
then the pilots and the colonel huddled over a map and
he showed them where he wanted to go. We got in and
the Negro started the auxiliary motor. The main motor
coughed and caught and the rotor began to turn and I
could feel the vibrations shaking up through my feet and
legs and back.

We lifted off and flew for maybe fifteen minutes before
the pilot began circling. Through the door I saw the
marker smoke, a blossom of yellow fog in the center of a
clearing. We made another circle and dropped. It was
like being in an elevator on the fortieth floor when somebody cuts the cables. We banked steeply and the patch-
work of paddies and trees was like a checkerboard spun

on a tabletop. The gunners were watching the trees, but I did not see any muzzle flashes. The colonel and the body-guard were leaning forward to get a better view, while Anson sat rigidly, his eyes shut.

We leveled off and came in fast and low, the wheels scudding over the treetops, and let down in a Buddhist graveyard. Almost before Anson, the last man, was out, the pilot pulled pitch and lifted away.

The graveyard was perhaps a quarter of a mile square. The Koreans were dug in everywhere, between graves and behind tombstones. The CO, a thickset captain, met us. A deep scar on his left cheek curved whitely through heavy black stubble, his lips were chapped and cracked, and he wore a helmet and flak jacket and carried an M2 slung over his shoulder. The colonel shook his hand and pounded him on the back. They talked in Korean, very rapidly, and the captain shook his fist at a pile of VC dead.

Most of the troops were still in their foxholes. Some were dozing, but most had the vacant hollow expression and glazed eyes that you often see after battle. The ground was strewn with debris, empty cartridge casings and ma-chine gun belt links, bandage wrappers, half-opened C-ration tins, ponchos, packs, metal ammunition boxes, in-trenching tools. We began taking pictures, but none of the Koreans looked at us, or even seemed to notice us. They just sat in the holes, clutching their weapons, and stared out beyond the perimeter. They were very different from Americans, who, no matter how tired or shell-shocked, usually try to pose and clown.

I found a boy, a machine-gunner, in a hole beside a

stack of Korean bodies. A belt of .30 cal. ammo was slung around his neck, the chin strap of his helmet was undone, and he was crying soundlessly, the tears squeezing out and down his cheeks one by one. On the lip of the hole was the machine gun, still loaded and pointed out toward the canebreak, with hundreds of empties littered about the feet of the tripod. The bodies had been wrapped in ponchos, but here and there arms and feet protruded, and beside one was a leg that had been severed at the thigh. The pants had been blown or ripped away, but the foot was still booted. I knelt and snapped the gunner, with the leg and the poncho-wrapped bodies in the foreground. The kid heard the camera clicking, and looked over at me, but did not stop crying, or in any way change expression.

I began to feel terrible and turned away from him. Sooner or later, on any story where there was a bad fight, I felt this way for a while. The good pictures and stories were always of the dead or the wounded or the grieving, and we were like vultures, we flourished on accident and catastrophe. Whenever you went out with people, no matter how much you liked them, you knew that to get good stuff some of them would have to be killed or hurt. The other way to look at it was that whatever happened happened, whether you were there or not, and, if you didn't report it, somebody else would. But sometimes I could not make myself see it that way.

I moved over to where Anson was shooting a pile of VC dead. With him were two American ANGLICO (Air Naval Gunfire Liaison) Marines. A pair of ANGLICOs was assigned to each Korean company. Most of the VC had been stripped, and they lay at odd angles, with legs and necks twisted into unnatural positions. They had died by all manner of means. Some had been stitched across the chest by automatic fire, others mangled by grenades, one had his jaw shot away, another had been decapitated, and a third had only a small neat hole precisely between the eyes. Several had crushed skulls, as if they had been clubbed or stomped, and two or three had erections. Anson was prodding one, who was lying face down, with his foot.

"Have a look at this bugger," he said. "Not a mark on him."

Anson got a boot under his shoulder and flipped him over.

"Fucking blast got him," one of the Americans said.

"I think it was taequando," Anson said. "See how his neck's broken?"

"Maybe," the Marine said.

I introduced myself to the Marines, whose names were Carson and MacCauley. They both had blue eyes and stubbly blond beards. I asked them what had happened.

"The mother fuckers tried to ding us," Carson said. "That's what happened."

We laughed.

"They come across in three waves," MacCauley said. He used his hands a great deal as he talked and Anson began shooting. "The first bunch had grenades. They hit us there." He pointed toward the high end of the graveyard, which merged with thick underbrush. "We had to pull in some, but then we got 'em out. The second was small stuff and more grenades, and the last one had a lot of automatic crap."

"Did they penetrate the perimeter?" Anson asked.

"No," Carson said. "They just moved us back some. But they sure scared the shit out of us."

"What time did it start?" I asked.

"0400."

"When did they break it off?"

"0600. Maybe a little later."

The colonel came up and said that he wanted us to photograph the captured weapons. We followed him to another, larger, pile of VC bodies. Beside them were rows of neatly arranged weapons. I counted two very dirty BARs, twelve carbines, an old French MG with a funnel-shaped flash suppressor on the muzzle and Chinese characters scratched into the receiver, two Chinese copies of Russian AK assault rifles with short barrels and long curved clips, and over a hundred stick grenades.

Anson photographed the colonel and the captain among the VC dead and conferring over a map, and I moved off with the Americans. They had been waiting for a Medevac chopper for the Korean dead — the wounded had been lifted out just before we arrived — and now both the Medevac and our ship were circling overhead. Over the radio we heard the pilots arguing over who had landing priority.

"My instructions were to return for VIPs in one-five minutes," one pilot said.

Carson was on the radio. "Fuck VIPs," he said. "We got bods down here. Over."

MacCauley gave a smoke grenade to a Korean, who pulled the pin and threw it into a clear place. It burst green. The Medevac chopper came in and the Korean captain tried to round up a crew to load the bodies. Nobody wanted to do it. The troops pretended they didn't hear, or that the captain was shouting at someone else. Finally the captain and the colonel walked to several holes and pointed to the men in them, who got up slowly, and, with obvious distaste, manhandled the bodies into the chopper. The captain picked up the leg I had photographed and stuffed it in the nearest poncho.

The Medevac ship lifted off and Carson called our bird back in. Anson didn't want to leave.

"We've got the dead," he said. "Now we need some action."

"All right," I said. I was sure the Koreans had decimated a VC battalion. I knew we would find more dead VC outside the perimeter, and thought that if they ran true to form, the live ones would be long gone. But they might leave a sniper or two behind, in which case we could get some action without too much danger to ourselves. We told the colonel and he said we could come out on the resupply chopper that night. He shook hands with us and climbed into the ship. The door gunner with acne gave us a thumbs up as they lifted off.

The captain showed us where we were on his map. We had to move through brush and jungle and across some paddies to a road, then down the road for a mile to hook up with some other companies. He sent a point platoon out, and in about five minutes the rest of us started. The troops were still grim, but had lost the glazed look, and they moved well in the brush, quietly and carefully.

There were many more VC bodies. I counted at least forty myself. Some had been hit by rifle or machine gun fire, but most had been shredded by artillery. All during the fight, of course, artillery had been coming in steadily up to within forty meters of their perimeter. Little bits of hair and clothing and flesh were stuck to tree trunks and bushes, and once I saw an arm hooked around a limb twenty feet overhead.

Anson was in good spirits. He began telling the ANGLICOs about a mythical French girl in Saigon, and they listened hungrily.

"How you git them French birds?" Carson asked. "All I ever seen is gooks."

"You must speak French," said Anson, who could barely manage a parlez-vous. "Then it's simple. They fall all over you."

We worked out of the trees and through a canebreak to the edge of a paddy field. The point platoon was two hundred yards ahead of us, moving toward a treeline and using a dike as cover. According to the map, the road we wanted ran along the treeline. The captain signaled a rest break, and we sat on top of a dike and took our packs off and lay back against them. I passed cigarettes around.

"How come you guys come out here?" MacCauley asked. "You don't have to, do you?"

"No," I said.

"It pays pretty good, I bet," Carson said.

"Fair," I said. "We aren't getting rich."

"You been out long?"

"Not too long," I said. "Three months. He has, though. He's short."

"I shall only do two more operations after this one," Anson said.

"Hey," Carson said. "Ain't you the guy who got zapped on that cutter? I read somewhere where some English guy got zapped."

"That was him," I said.

Anson pointed to the scar on his chin.

"Shit, buddy," Carson said. "If I was you I wouldn't go out no more no matter what they give me."

"You were in the service?" MacCauley asked.

"No," Anson said. "England doesn't have conscription any more."

"And you?"

"No," I said.

"Wouldn't that be a piss. You do your time out here and they fucking draft you and send you back," Carson said.

I stubbed out the cigarette and shut my eyes. White spots danced and slithered on the backs of the lids. The Marines stopped talking and I felt a gentle warm breeze. I sat up and rubbed my face. The Marines were lying there with their helmets off and eyes closed, Anson was wiping a camera with a chamois, and the captain was with his radio man behind the next dike, studying his map. Anson glanced up and smiled at me.

"About ready to push on, are they?" he said.

"I guess."

That was when it started. I heard a cracking sound, like a string of firecrackers lit somewhere in the next block, and saw a line of spouts of water two paddies ahead of us, and the treeline was winking with muzzle flashes. I threw myself forward and there was a short silence and then the cloth-tearing sound of incomings and the whines of ricochets. The earth was soft and damp against my face, and I began to count the number of stems in a clump of grass in front of my nose.

The Koreans reacted very quickly, they returned the fire almost instantly. I could distinguish at least two BARs working in steady regulation three-shot bursts amid the quick popping of the carbines on semi-auto and the solid cracks of M1s. Somewhere to the left a machine gun opened up and I wondered if it was the kid I'd photographed earlier. I felt around behind me for my camera bag and pulled it to me. Three red ants were climbing the strap. I watched them for a moment, then crushed them between my thumb and forefinger, and raised my head.

The captain was on the radio, talking to the point or calling artillery, and Anson was taking pictures of a 60mm mortar crew. He worked quickly, ducking from side to side for different angles, and, as always, I admired his coolness. He dodged down the dike and snapped a few of the BAR man, who did not notice he was there, then started across the paddy for the captain. The water was knee-deep and the gumbo sucked at his boots and the grain grabbed at his legs, but he ran hard, his body low and thrust forward and the camera bag swinging wildly from his shoulder. I got my camera up and centered him in the finder and he tripped, caught himself, straightened up, and I took the picture just as he was hit. His legs went out from under him, almost as if someone had clipped him in a football game, and he went sprawling sideways and forward. The camera bag flew open and equipment spewed out ahead of him and there was a quick mirror flash as a lens caught the sun. He flopped twice and was still.

I crawled toward him, wallowing in the muck and half-drowning in paddy water, but I think he was dead by the time I got there. I'm not sure. He was on his face, but I did not want to turn him over. All I could think of was to get him morphine. We always carried Syrettes of morphine with us, in our packs, and I crawled away for one. When I got back, a Korean medic was there. I showed him the Syrette — I was clutching it in my hand along with some mud and rice roots — and pointed at Anson's leg, but he shook his head.

After that I lost my sense of time. The rest of the action could have covered five minutes or half a day. I dragged Anson to a dike and spread a poncho over him, and found his cap, an Australian bush hat. I started to lift the poncho and put the hat with the body, but then thought that he wouldn't need it any more, some door gunner or embalmer would get it, and stuffed it in my pocket. At one point an air strike was called. Four camouflaged Phantoms came in and dropped 750-pound bombs on the treeline, strafed, and napalmed it. A spotter plane circled slowly but I couldn't hear the buzz of its motor over the firing. I took some pictures of the captain, the medic, and the ANGLICOs, but they were out of focus when I had them developed. Finally the firing died down — I found out later that the other Korean companies had hit the VC from the flank and killed four — and the Medevac ship came overhead. Carson was on the radio again. The pilot wanted to know how many he had to pick up.

"Two Korean WIA," Carson said. "One American KIA."

"One American?"

"Roger," Carson said. "They dinged this reporter."

"He was English," I said.

"What's the diff," MacCauley said. "They dinged him."

The chopper came down and I helped load the poncho. Then the Koreans were put in. The first man had his arm in a sling and insisted on climbing aboard without help. He was grinning. The second man was on a stretcher, and his face was drawn and his eyes closed.

A few minutes later MacCauley said they were sending a special chopper for me.

"Fine," I said.

I was sitting on the dike the captain and the radio man had used during the fight.

"You O.K.?"

"Sure," I said.

He offered me a cigarette and lighter.

When the H-34 landed he helped me gather the gear,

both packs and both camera bags, and load it. As I was climbing in, he slapped me on the shoulder, and Carson gave me thumbs up. We took off and rose quickly. The gunners were watching the treelines and did not pay any attention to me. For the first time I noticed that Anson's camera bag had been hit. There was a neat line of perforations across the front, four in all. I had put all the equipment I'd found back in, but had not noticed the hits. I thought I ought to send it to his family, but I did not know his parents' address. In fact, I didn't know if he had parents. I just knew that he came from London and wanted to go back there — although we always kidded him and told him that he'd be in Southeast Asia again in three months, that he couldn't bear the thought of a war without him there to photograph it. I also knew that he was an insomniac, that once or twice a week a piece of shrapnel worked its way out of his ass, that he became dangerous after a certain point in his drinking and had been known to pull a loaded gun on friends, that his jaw ached when it rained, that he was proud of the scars on his face and chest, that he wore his hair long because it was unmilitary and annoyed American officers, but that he kept in his desk a box containing the insignia of every outfit he'd ever gone into the field with, that he was in love with a Eurasian girl in Singapore, and that he idolized Capa and David Douglas Duncan. I had known him very well, I thought, but had not really known much about him.

The H–34 clattered on. We were high enough so that the gunners relaxed and I tapped one on the shoulder and asked where we were going. He yelled brigade, and I nodded, and settled back against the ship's side. The vibrations rattled me like an electric massage machine gone wild. I was marrow-tired and wanted more than anything to be someplace that was absolutely still, that did not batter me with noise. For no particular reason I remembered the Korean machine-gunner, the tears and the leg and the bandolier, and then I wondered how I would look if somebody should take a picture of me.

Kafka
for
President

IN DANANG I talked with Captain Hendricks, the head Marine Public Information Officer, about various Combined Action Companies. These were squad size Marine units posted in hamlets and villages with comparable size Popular Force units, the idea being that American aggressiveness and know-how would rub off on the Vietnamese, who would then be able to provide security for their own homes. As everyone was always saying, pacification, the uprooting of the Viet Cong infrastructure, was impossible without security.

Hendricks said a good CAC, one that hadn't received much publicity, was CAC 8, just off the road to Hoi An. The PIO, an ex-halfback from Ann Arbor and a recruiting poster Marine, heavy shouldered, lean, blond hair cropped so close the scalp gleamed, was delighted I was going to shoot the piece, and enthusiastically explained the operation. Without actually lying about anything he tried to leave me with the impression that the program was

achieving phenomenal success, was the answer to pacification. I did not blame him. In fact, I had expected it.

From his point of view it was a perfect story, one that
couldn't be told often enough. Instead of zippo-ing villages Marines were protecting them, instead of killing civilians or creating refugees they were helping, providing
security from the marauding Cong, medicines, no squatting prisoners, no crying mothers, only Christian brother-
hood and American social work. A story to which not even
the most militant Vietnik could take objection.

Hendricks sent me down to the 1/27 command post the
next morning, with a lance corporal as a bodyguard and
chauffeur. We went out by the short cut across the airfield,
past the revetments for the delta-wing F–102 Interceptors,
and a C–54 with the tail assembly removed, onto Highway
One. It was pocked with holes, some from mines, but most
from use. We passed a Marine company on a road sweep,
two long files of men, spaced out and walking with weapons at the ready, the machine-gunners wearing belts of
shining ammunition, pop art necklaces, around their
necks. Through towns with the familiar sloppy half-uni-
formed PFs lounging at the roadsides. I saw one tossing a
white phosphorous grenade in the air and catching it as
casually as if it were a rubber ball or an Indian club.
ARVNs guarded every bridge. They lived with their
women in dank straw-floored bunkers beside the road.
Five or six kilometers from Hoi An we turned off.

We drove into the 1/27 CP, a sandbagged and barbwire fortress on top of a sand dune, and I checked in with
the battalion executive officer, who turned me over to an

ancient goliath of a gunnery sergeant named Ingersoll. One of his ears was shot away, the other so cauliflowered even his own mother could never have recognized it.

I threw my stuff in the back of the gunny's mule. We went through a hamlet and out onto a country lane lined with coconut palms. The day was clear and cool from the recent monsoons. The palms ended and paddies stretched away to the treelines. A little boy was riding a water buffalo, whacking its neck and flanks with a stick. We passed a Buddhist graveyard, lumpy grass-covered mounds, a few headstones, one with ornate carving on it, and an old French blockhouse, a hexagonal bullet-pocked concrete bunker with beveled firing slits.

"How much farther?" I asked.

"Across the river," he said, and pointed ahead to a treeline.

I didn't see any river.

"Is this road secure?"

"Supposed to be," he said. "Ain't nobody been shot on it yet."

I laughed politely.

"Who you work for?" he asked.

"Free lance. I'm doing this job for the *New York Times*."

The gunny gargled and spat. I gathered he didn't approve of the *Times*.

"Sometimes I work for UPI," I offered.

"We don't get many reporters here."

I could see now that in front of the treeline was a river, spanned by a girdered bridge. On the near side was a sandbagged position. We clattered across. The Marine compound was a miniature of the CP, a living tent with sandbags halfway up the sides, a small stone house sprouting radio antennae, three sandbagged bunkers, one covering the bridge, the others the approaches from the hamlet beyond, a two-seat crapper that at first I mistook for a position, a shower made from a fifty-five-gallon drum perched on a stilt platform, the inevitable layers of concertina. A small basketball court had been scraped out behind the living tent and six Marines, one a giant Negro built along the lines of Jimmy Brown, were playing.

The hamlet beyond the wire was of the one-street variety. Thatched roof huts, dirt paths worn dusty smooth by bare feet, chickens, dogs, pigs, old women in black pajamas and conical hats, the usual. At the far end of the street sand dunes began, and on top of the first one was another French blockhouse.

"This-here's it," gunny said.

The basketball game broke up and the Marines, shirtless and sweating, crowded around the mule.

"Hey, gunny man," the big Negro said. "You bring the fuckin' beer?"

Gunny didn't answer, got out of the mule, and I followed him into the stone house, which contained several radios and a field phone, a desk, a couple of cots with air mattresses. A skinny, shirtless Negro, much lighter than the giant, was sitting by the radio reading a comic book, and a sergeant was writing at the desk.

"Sergeant Bernays," the gunny said.

"What do you know, gunny? You got beer?"

"This here is Mr. Bender from the *New York Times*."

Bernays stood up and we shook hands.

"Mr. Bender wants to look around a little. The major says you should extend him every courtesy."

"Glad to meet you," Bernays said.

I explained that I wanted to spend a day or two, shoot a few pictures. Bernays said that would be fine, they'd fix me a cot in here. He sent the light Negro, his name was Wright, to get my stuff.

Gunny left and Bernays introduced me to the Marines — there were seventeen of them, including one corpsman, a heavy squad — and we had lunch, C-rations heated on primitive stoves and washed down with Cokes and Dr. Peppers. The soft drinks were supplied by three Vietnamese houseboys, called Bugs Bunny and Fucky and Stinky, who brought them from a store in the hamlet for 15 piastres.

The Marines, except for Bernays, a veteran of the retreat from the Yalu in Korea, seemed very young and not particularly on the ball, high school dropout types. Hendricks had told me proudly that they were all proven veterans — CAC was not a place for malingerers, no one was considered for a CAC assignment until he had done six months in a line company. "These boys," he had concluded, "have all been in some good firefights." But they seemed very naïve, innocent, if you could apply the terms to someone who had spent six months in a Marine line company.

The living conditions, compared even to a Special Forces A-camp, were Stone Age. No refrigerator, no electricity, cots instead of bunks, C-rations instead of canned and frozen foods, beer came irregularly and in limited amounts, no hard liquor. And the defensive system seemed to me fairly flimsy. There was no artillery, not even any mortars or a machine gun, only two full automatic M–14s, which were notoriously hard to hold down. I asked Bernays about it, and he said, "Battalion says a detached squad don't rate no automatic weapons." The chief recreations were basketball, and, when it was warm, floating around under the bridge on air mattresses.

John Northup, a private from Chicago who had been drafted after two years of college because of low grades, and the corpsman, a boy named Lowenstein with a fierce Cossack mustache, offered to show me around the hamlet. They were evidentally the unit intellectuals, and were eager to get to know the visiting reporter. I asked Northup if there were other draftees in the unit and he said no. I asked him if he'd been surprised when they'd sent him to the Marines.

"Shit yes," he said. "I didn't even know the Corps took draftees."

"Are you glad now?"

"Are you kidding?" he said. "Christ, in the Army I'd have a soft job, be a fucking clerk or something. In the Corps everybody's a rifleman. Who wants to be a rifleman?"

We walked down the hut-lined street, past a well constructed stone house with a concertina roll for a front fence, a PF with a carbine standing guard. Lowenstein said it was the PF barracks. We stopped in front of a seamstress shop. There were two treadle sewing machines, one operated by an old woman and the other by a pretty girl wearing fresh light blue pajamas.

"That's Betty Lou," Lowenstein said, pointing to the pretty girl, who smiled at us coyly. "Prime slope cunt."

"Greer's giving it to her," Northup said.

"Which one's Greer?" I didn't know which names went with which faces yet.

"The big coon," Lowenstein said.

At the end of the street was a schoolhouse with a bare metal flagpole in the yard. Lowenstein said he held Medcap, or first aid sessions, here three times a week, and asked if I wanted to come. I said sure. We had a Coke at the store on the way back.

At 1700 Bernays sent out a patrol, six Vietnamese and six Marines, and I went along. The Marines wore flak jackets with no shirts under them and steel pots. Greer, a corporal, was the patrol leader. He showed me where we were going, tracing a route along the seashore — I had not realized we were so close to the ocean — and through some woods and a hamlet, which he said was deserted, and back to camp along the riverbank. His finger was the thickness of a rifle barrel, only blacker.

He put a Vietnamese on point, then an American, and so on. "If we don't alternate," he said, "the slopes bunches up on you. You gotta watch the little mothers all the time." I was in the middle with Lowenstein.

We moved out down the street, past the seamstresses' establishment — Greer grinned at Betty Lou and she giggled and Lowenstein said, "Look at the ass man" — and the store, through barbwire at the edge of town, by two positions which I assumed the Vietnamese manned at night, and along the dunes under the French fort. A dung-pit smell emanated from the fort and Lowenstein said, "That's the town shitter up there."

We hiked on, sinking into the fine deep sand, but it was pleasantly cool. A breeze blew over the dunes, smelling of sea salt and carrying the sound of waves. Greer motioned a redhead named Monday out onto the left flank. Monday had a bad sunburn and his bare arms protruding out of the flak jacket looked like half-cooked sausages.

I shot a good deal of film, trying always to include both Viets and Americans. The PFs in their motley uniforms — one was barefoot and two wore white tennis shoes and another faded jeans — and carrying carbines, looked like children out with Christmas present cap guns alongside the Marines.

After a half-hour's march we approached the woods, and people began to scan the treeline, train weapons on every modulation in the dunes. Suddenly Greer motioned us down. Lowenstein ducked behind a bush, drew his .45, cocked it. I got behind a low hummock of sand and knelt, shooting quickly. We waited a few seconds, crouched, poised, ready to fire and cringe and burrow into the sand, staring at the treeline, trying to detect some giveaway movement, some unnatural feature, but all I saw were bushes and palms swaying in the breeze.

Greer got us up, passed word back he'd seen something. I followed along after Lowenstein, my torso bent forward

as far as it would go without my falling on my face. I tried
to take bent-kneed steps, to make myself as small a target
as possible, and picked likely cover to dive behind.

Then we were at the trees and nothing had happened.
A bird squawked raucously and Lowenstein spun, his .45
held in front of him. The Vietnamese behind me laughed
and Lowenstein said, "Shut up, you fuckheaded slope."

We came into a clearing with the remains of a few
houses and huts, the hamlet shown on the map. The huts
had been burned down and all that was left were piles of
ashes and a few charred poles. The houses were roofless
and the walls were pocked and had holes in them such as a
round from a recoilless rifle might make. A stench hung
over the place, so cloying it was almost visible, and I
looked around for a body and saw a dead dog. Insects had
eaten out its eyes but its stomach had not burst yet, was
grotesquely distended.

We went on through a hedge and by another burned-
down shack into a new clearing. At the far end was a half-
destroyed house. A very old Vietnamese couple stood with
their backs to one of the shattered walls, their hands
clasped in front of them, while Greer and a PF covered
them. The other Marines and PFs set up a perimeter on
the edges of the clearing.

Lowenstein and I went to the house and I began taking
pictures.

"Not these two again," Lowenstein said.

"Yeah man," Greer said. "They the same ones."

"They won't leave," Lowenstein explained. "All the

people from here are supposed to be in the village, but these two stay here. We find them every time we patrol down here."

"Tell 'em," Greer said to the PF. "Why ain't they in the village where they belongs?"

The PF translated and the old woman began to cry, tears navigating down the creases at her eye corners and in her cheeks, and the old man shook his head and talked, slowly, and with dignity, addressing himself to Greer, his beard jerking as he spoke. He ended with a short bow. All through it his eyes had been expressionless, not calculating or begging or questioning or afraid, just flat.

"Say not have place go," the PF said. "Here home."

"Shit man," Greer said. "Don't give me that shit. Tell him again. Tell him if he stay here we gonna zap him sure. Tell him I seen him back there and I almost zap him this time."

"And tell that old lady to shut the fuck up," the corpsman said. The woman had not stopped crying.

"Can't we take them in with us?" I asked.

"We done that twice," Greer said.

When the PF had finished translating the old man went through his routine again. The woman kept wailing.

"He say not like village," the PF said. "Here home."

Greer drew his bayonet and held it to the old man's throat. The blade was black, but the cutting edges gleamed, were honed to a fineness worthy of a Gillette ad. Greer's biceps, black as anthracite and knotted, were thicker than the old man's neck. Greer put the tip of the bayonet under the old man's chin, forced his head up and back against the wall. The woman was on her knees, moaning and wailing. I was taking pictures.

"Tell him," Greer said. "The nex' time I zap him. Tell him I think they was VC here and I think the motherfuckers split while he talkin' and his old lady cryin'."

Greer drew the bayonet tip across the underside of the chin, behind the old man's beard, then wiped the blade on his pants and sheathed it. A few drops of bright blood dripped down the sparse hair of the beard. Without waiting for the PF to translate Greer said, "Aw right. Move out."

We formed up, followed a path out of the clearing. I glanced back just before plunging through the bamboo curtain. The woman was on her feet, dabbing at the man's chin with a rag of some sort, but she was still crying. Her man had not moved, was leaning against the wall, his head back and his hands folded in front of him.

We went up a small hill, the trail sandy, jungle undergrowth on all sides. The track veered every few yards and I closed up on Lowenstein, wanted him in sight in case we came to a fork. We reached the river, turned up it toward base. The water was still, layered with scum, perhaps a hundred yards across. The path now was packed, easy walking. We passed more shot-up houses, several deserted rice paddies. In front of a temple Greer called a halt. We found places beside the trail behind fallen logs and sat down with our backs against them.

Lowenstein said that just beyond here they'd gotten into a firefight about a week before, killed two Cong and gotten some papers that indicated the Cong were planning to hit the hamlet. One paper was a diagram of positions and another was a list of all the Marine and PF weapons. Greer, who was sitting with us, said, "Some of them mothers in that vil is Congs."

Monday, the sausage-armed redhead, had missed a VC at about twenty meters, shot an entire clip at him on full auto.

"Shit man," Greer said, laughing. "The Corps spends thousands of dollars teachin' the mother to shoot and he see a Cong and forget to aim."

Monday, several logs up the trail, heard and said, "Fuck you, Greer."

One of the Vietnamese brought us three green coconuts.

"He wants your bayonet," the doc said.

Greer hacked holes in the nuts and we drank the sweet cool milk.

Greer got us up, said to recon by fire. Instantly Monday cut loose a clip into the temple, sending up sprays of plaster and stone and tile. Lowenstein drew his .45 and assumed the classic pose of a pistol marksman, right arm extended but not rigid, feet apart and braced, left hand on hip, and began to shoot very deliberately at a coconut tree a few yards away. The PFs were clattering away with their carbines, but all were careful not to shoot at the temple. The one who had done the interpreting was trying to shoot down a cluster of coconuts, but hit several instead and the thin white fluid came down in streams. Greer walked up behind him and kicked him in the tail and shouted over the din, "This ain't no fuckin' nut hunt."

It was 1800 and getting dark quickly when we got back to base. A pair of PFs with a BAR and carbine were in one of the holes outside the wire. I was glad to see the BAR, hoped the PFs knew how to use it. Another PF pulled a roll of concertina across the trail behind us.

After dinner I talked with Bernays in the communications hut. The PF commander, a little sergeant named Hoa, was there, sitting on a blanket on the floor cleaning his carbine. Bernays talked to me about what he was trying to do in the village — put another room on the schoolhouse, get in some cheap cloth for the seamstresses, maybe get a battery-powered sewing machine, if there was such a thing, find some lumber for carpenters to make trunks with. He said all the Marines wanted trunks to send home souvenirs in. I got out my brandy flask, gave a shot to Bernays and one to Hoa, but he did not like it.

Later I walked with Bernays through the hamlet to check the sentries. They were in place, but the PFs outside the wire were smoking. We could see the coals from fifty yards, which meant so could a Cong crawling around out on the dunes.

"They ought to cup them," I said. "You can't see a cigarette if you cup it."

"I know," Bernays said. "I told them, but they didn't pay no attention and I ain't gonna tell them again. It's their fucking asses."

In the huts kerosene lamps burned softly. Bernays stopped in front of the seamstresses' hut, and said, "You in there, Greer?"

"Yeah man."

"The ambush goes out at 2300."

"I know, man."

"You getting any?"

Greer laughed.

We walked on and Bernays explained that every night he put out four-man Marine ambushes, listening posts really. He varied the times and places.

In the morning I went with Lowenstein to the schoolhouse for Medcap. He brought several bottles of antibiotic and vitamin pills and a huge bottle of antibiotic ointment, his instruments, and a cardboard box full of half-bars of soap. I asked him why he gave out the soap in pieces instead of whole, and he said, "I tried giving it to the fuck faces whole, but then they sell it. I want them to use it."

People swarmed into the school yard after us. Lowenstein set up his material on the steps.

"Watch how the little shits try to steal stuff," he said.

He got the people into line, children first. Some had nothing wrong, only wanted the big purple vitamins, but most had festering sores on the legs and ankles, or colds. Lowenstein explained that their blood did not coagulate well, that most were anemic, thanks to their poor diet, and any cut or insect bite was likely to infect. He yanked the scabs off with forceps, swabbed the wounds out with dabs of cotton dipped in the vaseline-like ointment, gave the patient a vitamin pill and an antibiotic pill, and watched while he took them. Several times he grabbed children by the necks and pried their mouths open and fished the pills out unswallowed. When that happened he dropped the pills on the ground and stamped on them.

"They take them home to their parents," he said. "I don't give a shit about their parents. If their parents got something wrong, they can come themselves."

Several children tried to sneak back in line, but Lowenstein picked them out, spanked them, threw dirt clods at them until they ran out of the yard. All the children laughed and giggled, except when having their scabs yanked off.

Next came the mothers with babies. Lowenstein gave both parent and child vitamins, and the mother a half bar of soap. Most of the babies had hideous rashes and scabs. Three had ringworm. Lowenstein cleaned them and shouted at each mother, "Wash the little shit. Use the fucking soap. He wouldn't have this rash if you washed him, you filthy pig."

The mothers nodded dumbly and smiled and tucked the soap inside their blouses.

"Half these kids oughta be in the hospital," the doc said.

Last were a few men, all war cripples or very old, and a dozen cackling old women. The men were very grave, smiled stiffly while their scabs were being yanked and bowed polite thank yous for their pills. The harridans squawked when Lowenstein hurt them. He could find nothing wrong with several and swatted them hard on the back and shoved them toward the gate, where they turned and spat betel juice at us and bawled what I was sure were the foulest of Vietnamese obscenities.

"They want pills," Lowenstein said. "And it gives them

the ass if I don't give them any. They're too fucking old to
waste pills on."

We collected the medicines and went back and I
washed very carefully, scrubbed at my hands and forearms
and face with a rough-grained medical soap, before lunch.

The afternoon patrol was to go in the opposite direction
from yesterday's, through an inhabited but unsecured
hamlet to a swift boat base. Swift boats were patrol vessels
that the Navy used to try to intercept smugglers. Bernays
said it was always a good patrol, because the Navy had a
generator and a refrigerator and plenty of beer.

Northup was on this patrol and I noticed written across
his helmet was *Kafka for President*. Almost all Marines
and soldiers wrote things on their helmets, but usually
they were predictably obscene or the names of their girl
friends.

"That's quite a slogan you have," I said.

"Shit," he said. "It's a fucking Kafkaesque war, isn't
it?"

I said I guessed it was.

Again a Vietnamese was on point, an American second,
etc. Bernays was patrol leader and Greer, unhappy at
missing the beer, stayed home. Bernays carried a carbine
he'd taken from a dead VC instead of an M–14. I asked
him if he always put a Vietnamese on point.

"Fucking A," he said. "It's their country. The least
they can do is run point."

Hoa went along too, and Monday told me, "That shit-face don't hardly ever stir out of the vil unless he thinks he'll get some beer."

We went behind the dunes in the other direction, the sea on our left flank this time, and into the inhabited hamlet. Bernays explained to me that within the month the Marines were going to depopulate the area, move the people either into his village or refugee camps. The place was filled with VC or VC sympathizers, which amounted to the same thing, and Battalion couldn't spare the men to start another CAC unit. The Marines had gotten intelligence about a VC meeting one night about a month before and had tried to ambush it. They'd been moving into the hamlet — he pointed to a burned down hut and scarred palm — when an old woman had set off the alarm, had seen or sensed them and started wailing.

"Just like that old bitch yesterday," Lowenstein said.

A machine gun had opened up, enfiladed the trail, killed one Marine and wounded another.

"Good kids," Bernays said. "I wanted to burn this place down the next day."

The people acted friendly enough, smiled at us, and the children ran beside the column and shouted and the dogs sniffed, but I noticed Bernays' carbine's safety was off. Hoa knew everybody, smiled and waved and stopped to chat.

At the swift-boat base we had a couple of cans of icy beer, more out of a sense of duty than any burning thirst, because it wasn't very hot. We took a different route home, worked along the shore of the stagnant lagoon. Bernays said we were looking for a VC .50 cal. machine gun which had been shooting at planes, and of course you never went back the same way you came out if you could help it. It was very hard going, vines and roots and walls of bamboo and stickers and wide ditches, mud-slimy trails and narrow dike tops. Insects dropped inside my shirt and limbs whipped across my face. My camera straps snagged every other step. The Marines were all tense, walked carefully with weapons held ready, but the Vietnamese appeared unconcerned.

They barged through the brush and talked noisily to each other and Hoa played a transistor radio. Nasal Vietnamese music preceded us at about a billion decibels. Bernays told him to shut it off. He pretended not to understand, but finally turned it down. I was hot and itchy and scared. The water, where we could see it through the curtains of vines, was filmed with a heavy scum of sick green. Reeds thrust up in little islands. Hoa turned his radio back up again, or anyway to my straining ears it sounded as if he did, and I said, "Why don't you take it away from him?"

"He'll bitch to his officers," Bernays said. "And then they bitch to Battalion and Battalion shits on me."

"I just hope there aren't any Cong in here," I said. "If there are, nobody's going to have a chance to bitch to anybody."

"At least they know where we are," Bernays said, grinning weakly. "They can keep away if they want to."

The radio played all the way back to the base but nothing happened.

*

That night Greer and Bernays planned an operation. There was an inhabited village on the river almost to the spot where it ran into the sea, well below the hamlet in which we'd found the old couple. They planned to move out in two columns at 0400 the next morning. One column would march down the beach, then sweep inland across paddies into the village, while the other would sneak down the riverbank and act as a blocking force. The two Marines decided they'd go with the beach column and let Hoa command the river group. I decided to go with the river group, because it had much less walking to do. I asked Bernays if he was going to brief Hoa tonight.

"Shit no," Bernays said.

"Why not?" I asked.

"Half his people will DD off to Hoi An," Bernays said. "They always bug off if they know about an operation. I'll wake him at 0300."

Bernays called Battalion, cleared the operation with them, gave them map coordinates. Then we walked over to the tent and he told the Marines. They bitched a little, but began cleaning weapons and laying out gear.

We went back to the house and I got Bernays talking about Hoa. He said he wasn't bad as PFs went. Anyway he trusted him. It was just that he hadn't had much training and most of his people had none at all. Hoa was very good at intelligence, at interrogating prisoners and assessing information. It was Hoa who had found out about the meeting in the village and he had killed one of the three Cong in the firefight. We had some brandy and turned in.

Bernays shook me awake at 0330. It was cold and completely dark. I got into my clothes and pulled on my boots, shivering. The Marines were forming up, joking and grumbling and cursing, but the PFs were quiet. Bernays made sure everyone was with the correct group, walked up and down the two columns shining a flashlight in each man's face, while we smoked last cigarettes.

Just outside the village we split up. Bernays' group plunged up the dune, by the French fort and over to the beach, while we worked toward the river. I was with Doc Lowenstein again. Hoa was ahead of him, then Northup. No one talked, but it seemed to me we were making enough noise to wake the dead, crashing through brush and tripping over roots. The PFs tinkled as they walked, grenades and clips ticking against each other and the eyelets in the webbing, sling swivels tapping stocks. The Marines had covered their swivels with green tape and made sure that grenades were secure, hung where they would not make noise, the handles held down by tape or rubber bands.

We found the river trail and stopped making so much noise. I could discern the outlines of the temple's winged roof as we passed it, but mostly I walked with my eyes down, picking my way, glancing up to make sure Lowenstein was close ahead. I developed the old familiar craving for tobacco, remembered on a night patrol in the rain once when I had put an unlit cigarette between my lips and sucked on it until it had gotten soggy and disintegrated.

We stopped for a minute, and two or three men ahead

a match flared and steadied and I could see Hoa lighting a cigar. He waved the flame out as casually as if we had been on a Sunday morning stroll. We started again and I saw the glowing tip bobbing. I was furious. I wanted to run past Lowenstein and snatch the cigar away and stamp it out. I did not think he was even making an effort to cup the thing.

We cut in from the river, climbed several dunes, legs driving in the slipping sand, and scrambled back down to the water's edge, and ahead always was the bright glow. We stopped again and another PF, farther ahead, lit a cigarette with a match flare I was sure you could see in Hanoi. Lowenstein moved up to Hoa and told him to throw the cigar away. His voice was tight with rage. We started again, still the bobbing glow. I wanted to beat the man, tackle him and sit on him and choke him and stuff the cigar down his throat. We crossed several clearings and I imagined a VC machine-gunner thumbing the safety off and aiming just below the glow and squeezing a burst and then raking down the column and I wondered if I would be quick enough to get down and scanned the dark trailsides for a place to dive.

But again, as with the transistor radio, nothing happened.

Dawn came and in the first half light we were still moving along the river. The pace quickened and we came to a hut with a kerosene lamp lit inside. Hoa sent two PFs in, and they hauled out an old man and two women, one with a baby, the other pregnant, and three small children. We herded them ahead of us. One of the children started to cry and Hoa slapped him. Another hut, a barking dog sent whimpering by a blow from Hoa's rifle butt. The PFs went in and collected an old woman, who came out rubbing her eyes, then went back for her conical hat.

By 0630 we had rounded up all the people who lived along the riverbank and herded them into a clearing in front of a schoolhouse. Two PFs guarded them. The other PFs and Marines were strung out on the riverbank behind logs and trees. I sat with Lowenstein on the schoolhouse steps and watched the prisoners. They squatted in the dirt, chatted. Occasionally one of the younger women would move away, turn her back and drop her trousers. The crones and children relieved themselves where they were. Several mothers breastfed their babies, and Lowenstein said, "Did you ever see such ugly tits?"

We heated C-ration ham and eggs and washed it down with coconut milk. Then I walked down the trail to where Northup had positioned himself behind a fallen tree. He had the radio, said Bernays hadn't had any contact yet, but had collected twenty-three women and children. I took a picture of a PF BAR man eating a bowl of rice, went back to the schoolhouse and stretched out on the top step, using my camera bag as a pillow.

I had just gotten comfortable when firing broke out. There were two bursts, and the BAR down the bank started. Several rounds whined overhead and smacked through the palm leaves. I rolled off the steps, crouched against the side of the schoolhouse, where

Lowenstein joined me. Another burst, followed by the concussive whump of hand grenades.

The Vietnamese civilians were in panic. The PF guards had disappeared. The old women jabbered and the children were crying. A woman scurried off up the trail and Lowenstein yelled at her to come back but she was out of sight around a bend. A young one, carrying her baby, broke, and Lowenstein drew his pistol and shot at her. The ejected round tinked against one of my cameras. Lowenstein shot again and missed and she was gone too, but he turned the pistol on the others. They stopped talking, none moved, even the smallest children, and watched him.

"Now stay where you fucking are," he said. "Or somebody's going to get hurt."

I got some good shots of him and the people. Several old women were squatting in piles of offal, had stained their pants. There was no more firing, and I ducked and dodged down the trail to Northup. He was lying behind his log, the muzzle of his M–14 poking around one end. I dropped beside him and asked what had happened. He didn't know. We waited perhaps five minutes — it seemed like a year — until Bernays called. Wright, the other Negro, had been wounded. One PF was dead. Two Cong killed, they were bringing in a female suspect. I went up the trail, told Doc to get ready.

A stream of civilians, exactly like the ones Lowenstein was guarding, ambled up the trail driven by PFs. The new group mingled with the old, squatted down, spat betel. Two PFs came up the trail carrying a body wrapped in a poncho. The hood was not snapped and blood dripped out of it. Then came Greer, carrying Wright in his arms as if he were a child. He also carried both rifles. Wright's flak vest, and Wright's webbing hung around his neck. Monday and Bernays prodded a young woman ahead of them, and each had an extra weapon, a carbine for Monday and an old bolt-action rifle for Bernays. The girl was rather pretty, neatly dressed in a fresh white shirt and black pajama trousers that weren't as baggy as most.

Greer laid Wright on the top step. He was pale, as if bleach had been poured over his smoke-colored skin, and his eyes were shut. His teeth were clenched and you could hear each breath distinctly. A hastily applied field dressing covered his right elbow and a tourniquet was tied around the biceps above. He groaned as Greer set him down. Doc had his bag open and went to work, took the dressing off and checked the tourniquet, straightened the arm and strapped it to Wright's side.

"You give him morphine?" he asked Greer.

"Yeah man."

"How many Syrettes?"

"One."

"How's it feel, Danny?"

"Shitty," Wright said.

"We'll have you out of here in a little."

Doc ripped Wright's trousers and jabbed a Syrette in his thigh. "Don't sweat it."

"I ain't."

Bernays said he thought the Medevac could set down in the school yard and told Monday to move the civilians.

Hoa and the interpreter were checking their IDs. Northup came up, said he had the Medevac. I could hear a chopper, a giant flapping in the distance.

It grew louder and an H-34 flew over and then a whining flapping and a Huey gunship, mounting four machine guns and fourteen rockets, came over so low the fronds trembled and a rotten coconut fell. Bernays threw out a smoke grenade which burst green, and the H-34 pilot's voice came over the radio saying he could make it and the ship lowered in. Greer picked Wright up and loaded him on and ducked away, and Wright gave us a thumbs up with his good hand as the chopper lifted, turned toward us, dipped its nose, and rushed at us across the yard like an airborne bull with whirling horns. It raised a wall of dust and knocked my hat off with the blast and barely cleared the school, then turned back across the river, straining for altitude.

I found my hat and dusted off my cameras. The Vietnamese were dust covered and clearly frightened. Hoa began checking their cards again. One out of every eight or ten did not have a card or had one that was out of date or possibly forged. These people were grouped to one side, and the others were released.

I sat on the steps with Doc and Greer and Bernays, who was gouging open a coconut, and asked what had happened. Bernays said they had been sweeping across a paddy, almost to the hamlet, and had come to a hut. Wright and the PF had gone in and brought out the girl in the neat blouse, who had tried to stall them. She had known a little English and did not have a card, went

through a long story about how she had lost it. Greer and
Bernays had listened to her, and the PF and Wright had
gone around behind the hut and surprised two armed
Cong trying to climb into a well. The Cong had killed
the PF and wounded Wright, although Wright had
wounded one of them. They tried to run away, the un-
hurt man helping his friend, and Greer had come around
the hut and cut them both down. Then he had grenaded
the well. They'd left the bodies there.

Doc said Wright's elbow had probably been shattered,
he would lose most of the use of it, if they didn't have to
amputate. Greer was eating from a tin of steak and po-
tatoes, and did not say anything, did not appear to be
listening to us, just moved the plastic spoon back and
forth between can and mouth.

When Hoa had finished with the civilians, he com-
mandeered six sampans with boat women, and we loaded
ourselves and the dead PF and the suspects, eight of them
including the girl, and began to pole up the river toward
base. I asked Bernays if it wasn't dangerous going up the
river like this, and he said no, we'd swept one side, and
C-company had positions all along the other.

The sun was out but not too hot and I rested in the bottom of the sampan and let myself relax with the thrusting and gliding of the poling and felt the sun on my face.
I started to doze again and then jerked awake at the sound
of two explosions. I couldn't place what they were, and
sat up, almost tipping the sampan over, in time to hear a
third, and see a great fountain of scummy brown water

lift up in front of a sampan filled with PFs. The water settled lazily. Bernays was laughing at me.

"They're fishing," he said.

A PF in another sampan stood up, his legs braced, the narrow craft tipping, the boat woman balancing with her pole, and pulled the pin from a grenade and threw it out ahead. Another explosive lifting of dirty water. Ahead of the first sampan the water was dotted with silver spots, fish that had risen to the surface, killed by the concussion. One fish swam crazily along the top of the water, its head out like a girl who doesn't want to get her hair wet, and a PF dove in after it.

It was almost 1300 when we got to base. The boat women drove the bows of the sampans into the shore mud and we unloaded. The PFs herded the suspects into a one-room hut with no windows. All of the prisoners were women, but the girl Greer and Bernays had picked up stood out. She was younger, better dressed, much cleaner, and did not talk and cackle with the others, but walked by herself, her arms tied behind her, head up. The last sampan to be unloaded carried the dead PF and many dead fish. The hood of the poncho was crusted with blood, but had stopped dripping, and smelled of fish.

Lowenstein and Northup and I opened some cans and sent Bugs Bunny for Cokes.

"What happens now?" I asked.

"We'll torture them, probably," Northup said.

"That's one thing Hoa is good for," Doc said. "He can make the little fuckers talk."

"And after that?"

Northup shrugged.

Bernays came over and Doc asked, "When do we start?"

"Start what," Bernays laughed.

"You know fucking well."

"Hoa wants to let them stew awhile."

After lunch we shot baskets until the torturing began, at about 1500, in a small dark hut. I tried to bring my cameras, but Bernays shook his head. The hut was too dark to have gotten anything anyway.

Hoa and the PF translator were the only Viets there, but most of the Americans crowded into the room. The only furniture was a straight-backed chair, occupied by Hoa, and a low wooden bench. Greer brought the girl in, her hands still tied behind her. She looked at us, her glance seeming to stop for a moment on each face, but did not appear frightened. Hoa spoke to her in Vietnamese and she sat down on the bench. He questioned her for a half hour, making notes in a little spiral pad.

"What's she saying," Bernays asked.

"Nothing," the interpreter said. "Say not live here. Visit friend. Lie."

Hoa kept repeating the same questions and the girl shook her head, answered briefly or not at all, looked down. Hoa's voice became angry, she shook her head again. Hoa nodded to Greer. He untied her hands and forced her to lie down on the bench on her back. Then he tied her hands and feet together under the bench.

Hoa spoke to her again, his voice level and smooth. She shook her head. Her eyes were shut. Hoa nodded to the translator, who went outside and dragged in a five-gallon water tin. Hoa pulled a washcloth-size rag out of his pocket and a bar of soap, and placed the rag over the girl's face. He lit a cigarette and tipped back his chair.

"She's scared pissless now," Monday said.

"You'd better believe it," Doc said.

"I don't know," Northup said. "You can't tell. She may have been expecting this."

"I don't give a shit if she was expecting it or not," Monday said. "She's gotta be scared. She knows Hoa ain't fucking around."

The girl turned her head and the cloth fell off. Hoa leaned forward and his arm whiplashed out and his open palm popped into her cheek. Tears gathered in her eyes. Hoa put the cloth back and began to question her. She shook her head, the cloth fell, he slapped her again. She shouted something at him and he laughed, replaced the cloth, nodded to the interpreter.

Greer held the girl's head in his massive hands and the interpreter poured some water onto the cloth. The girl gasped. Hoa leaned forward, rubbed soap into the wet cloth until it lathered, then nodded to the interpreter again. He poured water, and the girl began to struggle, to heave and twist her head against Greer's vise grip. Her hips twisted as if she were doing a belly dance, and Monday said, "Look at that. She looks like she's humping."

Hoa took the cloth away and the girl jerked her head from side to side, spluttering and sucking air, and threw up. Soap bubbles were mixed with her vomit, and some of it went down her neck and onto her blouse. She kept gasping and vomiting for some time more or less simultaneously. Then Hoa questioned her and again she shook her head. He put the cloth back and rubbed in more soap and nodded to the interpreter.

It went on like that for an hour and a half before she broke. All the Marines but Greer and Bernays had left, though from time to time they dropped in to find out how things were going. Finally, after the interpreter had emptied two tins of water and Hoa's soap was worn to a sliver, the girl began to babble and cry. I thought her nerves had snapped, that she was out of her head, but Hoa smiled at Bernays. He asked more questions, which she now answered volubly, and wrote furiously in his notebook.

The interpreter translated in snatches. She was a VC schoolteacher. She had been trained in North Vietnam. She was new in this area. She had relatives here. She was born in Quang Ngai. Hoa wanted to know how many local VC there were, what units, and did not like her answer, put the cloth back. She gave the names and numbers of some local force units and Bernays and Hoa seemed pleased. Then Hoa asked who were VC sympathizers and agents in town. She hesitated and he dangled the cloth. She started to talk. Hoa looked sharply at Greer, then at Bernays.

"Betty Lou, she say," the interpreter said.

Greer didn't say anything, but put one of his huge hands on her throat and began to squeeze. Her breath came hoarsely as he bore down on her windpipe. Hoa motioned him away, but he did not release her, just lessened the pressure slightly. She spoke quickly.

"Betty Lou fucky VC," the interpreter said.

Greer was looking down at her and I shall never forget his expression. There was something of the hurt animal in it, a look such as you sometimes see on the faces of the mortally wounded just after they have been hit, a sudden and complete comprehension of the worst, but also the loss of bearing and perspective, the enveloping numbness, that comes with severe shock.

"Knock it off, Greer," Bernays said. "Take a break."

Greer stood up and went outside.

Hoa kept questioning. Betty Lou was the one who had furnished the diagram of the positions and the list of weapons. Two other women had relatives in the local VC. Hoa wanted to know if there were any plans to attack. She said no, one of the VC the Marines had killed had been the local CO, and anyway the VC knew the Marines had found the diagram. Hoa put the cloth back over her, but she repeated the story exactly.

It was past 1800 when they finished. Bernays said to come get some food, they'd work on Betty Lou after dinner. One of the PFs had been sent to arrest her and the other two women when the girl had talked.

I was not hungry, and walked out onto the bridge and watched the water and the sunset. Two Marines were manning the position at the far end. I could hear the murmur of their voices but not what they said. A 106mm recoilless rifle fired somewhere across the river, made a long whining whooshing and detonated in the distance.

I went into the tent. Lowenstein and Monday and

Northup and a lance corporal named Mitchell were playing hearts. Greer was lying on a cot in shorts. I stopped
and started to say something, but his eyes were closed.
Northup motioned me away with a wave of his hand and
shook his head.

After Bernays and Hoa had eaten they started on
Betty Lou. They took her into the interrogation hut and
lit a lamp. Hoa did not go through the polite prelimina-
ries, just had the interpreter tie her down. She was very
frightened. Her legs and arms trembled. Without Greer
there to hold her head, Hoa had to get out of his chair and
help with the work. After one long douse she was crying
hysterically, and Hoa began to question her. Yes, she
had made the diagram. Yes, she did have a VC boyfriend.
She named other VC sympathizers.

Hoa was writing again. The lamplight flickered across
his face. I looked to the door and Greer stood there. He
was in the shadows and I could not make out his expression. I watched him for some time, but he did not move.

Hoa asked the girl where she met her boyfriend. No
answer. He slapped her. No answer. He put the cloth
on, soaped it, poured water. She gasped, vomited. In a
rice paddy on the other side of the river. When? How
did they arrange the meetings? She was sobbing and he
poured more water and she retched. The boyfriend was
a farmer. He had papers. When did they meet? He
slapped her very hard. Every other Thursday when she
went to Hoi An to buy cloth. She had to walk to Route
One, where she caught a Lambretta bus. He met her in
the afternoons on the way back.

"Maybe can kill," Hoa said.

Bernays nodded.

Hoa continued questioning her, going over the same ground again and again, trying to catch her in a lie, or get her to expand the information she had already given. I was very tired, had a headache, and did not want to hear any more. Greer was in the doorway as I left, and I said good night, but he did not answer.

During the night it rained.

The next morning was fresh and bright. The sun was out and the air was cool and very clear. I ate with Bernays, asked him what would happen to the prisoners. He said they would be turned over to Battalion, a jeep was coming for them in an hour or so. I said I was about ready to shove off myself, I had plenty of material, and he said he'd call Battalion and ask for transportation. He didn't think there would be room for me in the first jeep. I asked if they were going to send all the prisoners, and he said no, just the girl, who was really hard core, and Betty Lou. The others would go to a refugee camp, but there was no hurry about it.

I played basketball with Monday and Northup, then shaved and packed my rucksack. I was just finishing when the jeep came for Betty Lou and the girl. It carried two Marines. The driver held a shotgun and the guard an M–14.

A PF brought out the prisoners. Both were red-eyed from the soap but otherwise looked all right. The girl had managed to clean most of the vomit off her shirt, and had recovered her resolve. In fact, they both looked resigned, but sullen and determined and not scared. I thought the girl must have given Betty Lou a talking. Their hands were tied.

They got in the back seat and the Marines tied their bonds to the seats. Most of the CAC Marines were gathered around, including Greer, who stood on Betty Lou's side, trying to catch her eye. Both of the girls stared straight ahead. The driver started the motor. Bernays was on his side, his hand on the windshield post.

"Tell gunny to bring out the beer," he said.

"Gunny ain't supposed to come out here today," the driver said.

"Yes he is," Bernays said. "He's coming to pick up this reporter." He nodded at me. "Remind him we ain't had no beer in two weeks."

Greer stepped up to the side of the jeep and put his hand on Betty Lou's shoulder. She turned and spat full in his face.

"All right," the driver said. "I'll tell him."

Greer stepped back and wiped his arm across his face. The guard twisted around in his seat, put the muzzle of his rifle under Betty Lou's chin, said, "Cut that shit out, you hear?"

The driver put the jeep in gear and pulled away. Greer went into the tent.

"Fucking slope cunt," Lowenstein said.

The group broke up, some going to the basketball court and others into the tent or to the village. Doc started off for Medcap and asked if I wanted to come. I did not.

Gunny Ingersoll drove up promptly at 1100.

"You bring beer?" Bernays asked him.

"What beer?" Gunny said. "There ain't a can of beer in the whole fucking Battalion."

I shook hands with all the Marines who were nearby, and thanked Bernays. He said to come back any time. I threw my gear in the back of the mule and got in. Gunny turned around and we started out onto the bridge. Greer was standing on the edge in the middle, wearing only shorts. He looked like a sculptor's model for a black god. Gunny slowed as we went past and I said, "So long, Greer. Take it easy."

"Yeah man," he said.

We reached the other side and I turned for a last look at the place. Greer sprang away from the bridge and flung out his arms and arched his back, hung suspended, then nosed over and arrowed for the water and hit and a plume of spray geysered up behind his heels. He stayed down until I was holding my own breath and the bank threatened to interfere with my line of sight. I stood up in the bouncing mule, gripping the windshield and the seat back, and he came up, snorted, and swam toward the bank.

A
Birth
in the Delta

THE COMPANY was spread
out behind a series of dikes, taking a lunch break. The
sun thrust down, glared with steady eye-aching intensity
off the muddy paddy water. Some of the men had taken off
their shirts, others wore undershirts, which were dark with
sweat. Now, resting, they had all taken off their helmets.
They were all also caked with mud to their thighs. The
mud was drying in the sun, beginning to crack.

The company had been in the field in the Delta for a
week, plowing across an interminable series of paddies, always working through the muck and never along the hard
packed dikes, because the dikes were where you ran into
ambushes and mines and booby traps. Before this operation they had had a one day stand-down, complete with
warm orange sodas and new uniforms, after having been
in the field for ten days. Before that they had had a one
day stand-down . . . etc.

The headquarters element was grouped in the center,

around the company commander, Captain Harkness. Harkness looked to be perhaps eighteen, with the tanned athletic aspect of a lifeguard or an assistant tennis pro, his face smoothly brown and his hair thick and blond, close cropped. His appearance was somewhat deceptive, for actually he was twenty-six, a veteran commander, now in the eighth month of his second tour. A paratrooper, an instructor at ranger school, a survivor of two dozen bitter firefights in the Central Highlands two years ago. He was studying the map — it often seemed to him he had spent the major part of his adult life studying maps — and half listening to the desultory luncheon conversation going on around him.

"I'll trade you ham and eggs for them Salems," said Corporal Blacksides.

"Fuck that," said Top Sergeant Himmlemann.

"You can have my coffee too."

"Shit. I got plenty of coffee."

"They give me the fucking shaft. I'm too fucking short." That was PFC Leyba, the radio man, who was scheduled to leave in three days. "They shouldn't have sent me to the field again. Fucking Roth didn't go on no operations, and I'm shorter than he was."

"Roth was a fucking fuck-up, Leyba," said Spec 4 Burns, the medic. "We need you."

"Fuck you."

"Ask the old man. You're indispensable, Leyba. They ain't never gonna let you go home."

"Watch your fucking lip. I'll fucking bust it for you."

"I'll give you my peaches."

"I don't know."

"Peaches, you asshole. You don't even like Salems."

"I got to think about it."

"Fucking eighty more days," said Rifleman Upshaw. He drew a line through the number 81 on his helmet. Many of the troops' helmets were virtually covered with numbers.

"You can't cross it off yet," said Private Prissholm, who was on his first operation. "We're not through the day."

"I can cross it off if I fucking want."

"Of course you can," Prissholm said. "But it doesn't mean anything."

"Shit."

"A can of peaches for a pack of fucking cigarettes, you dip. You don't even like the fucking brand."

"Maybe I don't like peaches neither."

"Don't shit me, Top."

"I never shit nobody."

The captain glanced at his watch, went over the map another time, making sure he had not missed some obvious ambush site. "All right, Top," he said. "Tell 'em to put it on."

"Where do we go now?" Prissholm asked.

"Across some more fucking paddies, you idiot," Upshaw said. "Where do you think we're going? On fucking R and R?"

"Put it on," Top was bellowing.

"Maybe we'll get us a fucking vil," Leyba said. "I like to burn them hootches."

"Rape, loot, pillage, burn," Burns said.

"Lay off that shit," Top said. "There ain't no fucking TV cameras around."

Men were standing up, slowly, drawing each move out, feeling the sweat begin to run again as they donned shirts, slid packs and webbing over shoulders, fastened buckles, slung ammunition containers and belts of machine gun bullets, placed the hated weights of the helmets. Harkness gave instructions to the platoon lieutenants over the radio. The point element, which was several dikes ahead, moved out. The company unfolded forward like an opening accordion. Harkness checked to either side that the flank security was out. They had not had a contact for two days, and he was not particularly expecting one, but he knew you got hit when you expected it least, and worked constantly to keep himself and his troops alert. Two or three kilometers ahead of them a treeline shimmered in the heat, a dancing band of cool across the glare. It could almost have been a mirage, but he knew from the map it was real enough.

It was headquarters' turn to move. One by one the men went over the dike, hesitated, and stepped down into the muck on the other side. The Delta was the most work of any place in the country, Harkness thought. In the mountains at least you were on firm ground. There were always twice as many heat exhaustion cases here. Several times he thought he had come to the end of his own rope. But you learned how to move in the muck, how to hop from one rice plant to the next and never, almost never, slide off into the gumbo, which might be knee or even thigh deep.

They slogged through the paddy and over the dike and

into the next one and the sun kept pouring down. Some of the men wore sunglasses, but most did not bother. Glasses fogged up and you sweated so much they were impossible to keep clean. Every so often a man fell down, slipped off a rice plant and lost his balance and sprawled forward or sideways into the water and mud, then scrambled up swearing. They crossed one deep canal. They held rifles and ammunition overhead, but a machine-gunner, a Negro named Dillard, slipped going up the far side, slid back into the water on his chest, dragging weapon and ammunition through the ooze. Two men helped pull him out and they stopped while he cleaned the gun, wiped off the belts.

After an hour they stopped for a five minute break.

"I'm almost out of water," Prissholm complained. Most of the men were drinking deeply, carried four or five canteens on D-rings and webbing.

"Don't look at me, dickhead," Upshaw said.

"I wasn't asking for any. I just wonder when we'll get a re-supply."

"Shit," Upshaw said.

"Maybe tomorrow," Burns said. "Maybe tonight. Maybe never."

"I could pill this paddy water."

"Sure," the medic said. "Put enough pills in piss and you could drink it."

"Don't shit this dickhead, doc," Himmlemann said. "He might try it."

"Top," Harkness said. "Make sure they're taking their salt."

"Right."

"I got plenty of salt pills," Burns said. "Iodine too. If anybody needs them."

"Good, doc," Harkness said.

"Blacksides, have you got some extra water?"

"How much you got left?"

"About half a canteen."

"You got plenty. Tell me when you're out."

"Thanks a million."

"Any time, dickhead."

"This fucking operation eats shit," Leyba said. "It sucks."

"Nobody'll argue with you about that," Burns said.

"It's a goddamn ratfuck. I'm too short to get zapped on a ratfuck."

"You aren't going to get zapped."

"Fucking A I ain't. But you can't never tell."

"Don't sweat getting zapped, Leyba. I'll fix you up."

"Shit, doc. You don't know how to get a Band-Aid on straight."

"Well, motherfuck, just hope you don't have to try me."

"Now don't get pissed off."

"O.K.," Harkness said. "Let's move out. Get 'em moving, Top."

Harkness called ahead to the point and out to the flanks on the radio, told his people to stay alert, to watch the treeline. They were less than a kilometer away now. The map showed several hootches, which did not necessarily mean that there were people, or even hootches any more. However, Harkness was aware of how naked his people were coming across the paddies, how they might look through a pair of binoculars or a telescopic sight. He called Battalion, made sure they wanted him to push on. They did.

"It's typical," he said to Sergeant Himmlemann. "They haven't got a fucking blocking force so anybody in there can DD if they feel like it."

Himmlemann, his bull neck luminous with sunburn, the color of windblown coals, was too busy hopping from rice clump to rice clump to answer.

Leyba, slogging behind the captain, bent under the weight of the radio, loathed Harkness, focused his hate at a point between the captain's shoulder blades. He hated Harkness for bringing him out again, was sure he could have gotten him a dispensation. In fact, he had hated the captain for eight months, ever since Harkness had come to the company and made him a radio operator in the first place. The radio cut down into his shoulders and tendons, caused a burning sensation and numbness, almost as if the straps were eating their way through his flesh and sinew. He had humped the captain's radio and never gotten used to it: it was his ball and chain, an extra thirty pounds of knobs and transistors and batteries that nagged him like a lead growth. He had nightmares where he was drowning in a canal, floundering face down in brackish water, the weight on his back pressing him inexorably toward the muddy bottom. He thought of shooting Harkness if they got into a contact, a recurrent and favorite daydream. He had read about things like that happening, good soldiers shooting unjust officers in the field, in men's magazines. As far as he knew it had never happened in their brigade or their division. But there was always a first time. But they might catch him, and then he wouldn't deros, wouldn't ride the freedom bird, they would put him in LBJ, the Long Binh Jail. If he wasn't so close to leaving he wouldn't even mind that. Sometimes he thought anything would be better than the radio, than humping the boonies week after week with that dead weight on his back. He would shoot Harkness without a qualm if it weren't such bad percentages with only three days left.

Private Prissholm was simply miserable. He had gotten over being frightened — the first few days out he had been carried by sheer nervous energy, had imagined every odd shape and terrain feature concealed his doom, had not slept ten minutes — but now he was only tired, indescribably weary through his thighs and calves, and thirsty. How was he supposed to have known most of the water here was so saline as to be undrinkable, even when liberally laced with purification tablets? And even if he had known about that, how was he to have guessed that re-supply would be so erratic? He assumed that somehow things like water and food got taken care of. This was, after all, the American Army, and the one thing everyone admitted Americans were superior at was logistics. That was supposed to be our genius. Six million cans of hair spray for the Saigon PX and air bases with ten thousand-foot runways of solid reinforced concrete every twenty miles up and down the country, but no water for one infantryman in the Delta.

He imagined a confrontation with the battalion lieutenant colonel, a mean eyed Swede who affected a fatherly attitude, called everyone from his most senior major on down lad, in which he, Private Prissholm, told the colonel that it was a fucked up Army that expected its troops to fight without water, and the colonel, amazingly, agreed with him, assured him it wouldn't happen again. Momentarily Prissholm was pleased with the vision, his victory, and then he thought that he was deluding himself. He was losing touch with reality. He was Michael Edwin Prissholm, college graduate, political science major, former vice president of the sophomore class, and all of this, the colonel, the water, the muck, the heat, cretinous Sergeant Himmlemann, Leyba the obvious psychotic, Harkness who was running for eagle scout, everything since basic training, since induction, all of it was unreal, had nothing to do with the real world and real people. The only way to survive mentally was to turn off his mind.

Burns, the medic, was content. He was light, very lithe, and he was not weighted down with ammunition as were the other men, so he hopped easily, mechanically, from plant to plant. He had learned long ago how to turn off his mind, divert its focus, on marches like this, to concentrate his physical attention on the next step, never farther ahead than two steps, while he let the thinking part of his brain slip off on little trips. Burns was always well equipped with marijuana, and had even devised a way of taking it in public. He smoked Kools, the most noxiously mentholated of cigarettes, and he had discovered that by carefully repacking the tubes with a mixture of tobacco and grass the pot odor was lost in the menthol. He was so expert at this that it was completely impossible to tell one of his repacks from an original until you smoked it. He had smoked frequently in front of the captain, and had even considered offering him one just to see what would happen.

Now Burns was imagining being rich. He was a licensed chiropractor, a profession he had chosen for its large remunerative potential. He had just completed school when the Army drafted him. At first he had been indignant — at being drafted at all, then at not being treated like a doctor. They had no right to make him a mere medic while doctors were automatically officers and never left the air conditioned hospitals. But then he had gotten over here and all he cared about now was living through his tour so that he could go home to San Jose and start his practice. His Army record might even help bring in patients. Burns was a good California boy, born and raised there, and he happily imagined a weekend house in Santa Cruz where he could surf all year around. He would need a wet suit, for the water there was very cold, the Japan current brushed the coast at that point, but the surf was excellent. The house in Santa Cruz and a sports car — today he was torn between a Jag XK-E and a Corvette, with one of the new Porsches running slightly behind — to get him there from San Jose. Maybe a helicopter. He had never thought of a personal chopper before. He would learn to fly, buy one of those Loaches like the colonel had. They couldn't be all that expensive. He pictured the house on the cliff overlooking the beach and the long waves breaking and his Loach skimming in over the hills and landing in front of the house.

Harkness was getting worried. They were closing on the treeline and he was reflexively worried. He had been shot at from too many treelines. He pushed the point out a little farther. In a few minutes he would begin to recon by fire, let his lead platoon shoot. If you shot first, even if you were wild, they would sometimes open up themselves when you were still out of effective range, give their position away. Usually, of course, they weren't there at all. And this time there might be civilians. Down here in the Delta there was always a chance of that. There were not supposed to be, Intelligence said they had all been moved out, but few things worked out the way they were supposed to.

It was precisely then that the point man in the lead squad, which was only 150 hundred meters from the treeline, climbed across a grassy dike and tripped off a booby trap, a grenade with a wire attached to the pin. The fuse had been removed, and the grenade detonated instantaneously, blowing off the point man's right foot and sending fragments into his inner thighs and groin. The man behind got a few pieces in the chest.

There was a moment of general confusion, men stopping and crouching, trying to place the explosion, fix its type and source. Then a few of the new ones scurried headlong for cover, for the protective backsides of the dikes, and the platoon sergeants shouted at them to stay calm, to watch for trip wires. Harkness called to the point squad leader, asked what had happened.

"Fucking booby trap. Two WIA."

"Who?"

"Fraily. And that new guy. Walinski. He got a foot blown to shit and got it in the nuts."

"He was on point?"

"That's affirm."

It was usual practice to put the new men on point. It slightly minimized the risk for the veterans. The new men either died or were wounded or learned quickly enough to live until there was someone newer than themselves.

Harkness called for a Medevac, then called Battalion, told the colonel what had happened. They discussed the best way to proceed. They had to assume there were unfriendlies in the treeline. They could try to flank it, then drive in, or call in arty and air.

"There might be some civilians," Harkness pointed out.

"I know."

"S-2 says they got them out."

"I know that's what S-2 says. The province chief told him." The colonel paused. "It's up to you, lad. You're the man on the spot."

"Let's get arty and the gunships then. Maybe we can get an air strike."

It was better them than us, Harkness thought. Though there might not be any of them there at all. But if there were and the place wasn't prepped he'd take more casualties getting in, and probably have nothing to show for his blood. The advantages of position, of camouflage and fortification and field of fire, were all with the enemy. He knew of at least two company commanders who had been relieved after such incidents. It was fine to be thoughtful of the civilian population, but not at the expense of the kill ratio.

He called up to the lead platoon, had it withdraw a hundred meters. Within five minutes white phosphorous marker rounds began to drop in the trees and paddies in front. One was short, hit right on his platoon's old position. He adjusted the fire, called in the high explosive.

They brought the wounded back to the captain's position. Burns had gone forward immediately after the explosion, tied off Walinksi's leg. Fraily was a Band-Aid case, a question of picking out a few splinters. Burns gave Walinski two morphine shots, which did not seem to have much effect. He kept trying to cluch the mangled wreckage of his genitals. Every so often the stump of his right calf jerked, as if a doctor were testing his reflexes.

Prissholm watched Walinski in fascination. Walinski was the first seriously wounded man he had seen. Prissholm felt giddy, lightheaded. He was breathing rapidly, through his mouth. Walinski had come only a week before he had. He, Prissholm, had been incredibly lucky to be assigned to HQ rather than a regular squad. He would have to keep in Harkness's favor no matter what.

Leyba, as did the others, with the exception of Burns, ignored the wounded. They were out of it, it did no good to look at them. Leyba sat on a dike top, the radio on his back, connected to the captain by the flexible umbilical cord of the microphone, and hunched over, looked as if he were trying to touch his forehead to the ground between his feet, made himself as small a target as possible. There had been no incomings yet, but there might be any second, or short artillery rounds, or the fucking gunships. Cobra pilots didn't know their dicks from their assholes. Harkness stood beside him easily, map in one hand, the mike in the other, occasionally shading his eyes with the map, giving corrections and instructions to the artillery and then the gunships as casually as if he were conversing in a living room. Harkness was forever exposing himself — he probably thought he had to set a fucking example or something — and Leyba, because he was the radio man, usually got exposed with him. Leyba imagined a short round hitting out in the paddy in front of them, dinging Harkness but sparing him.

While the gunbirds were working the Medevac came in and loaded the wounded. Walinski was crying and Fraily was grinning.

The gunships expended, flew off, and the artillery started again. Salvos of 105 and 155 alternated. Whole trees were blown up by the 155s, cartwheeled through the air.

"Sock it to 'em," Upshaw said.

"Look at that shit," Blacksides said. "That's beautiful. Beautiful."

"You know Charlie's shit is weak now," Upshaw said.

Prissholm was watching the treeline with the others, but was unable to keep from wincing at each series of explosions. Several fires were started.

"It's burning. Beautiful."

"Burn, baby, burn."

"Fucking arty is O.K."

"Except when they're short. Sometimes those dick-heads can't hit a bull in the asshole boresighted."

"They're beautiful today."

When the shoot was over Harkness moved them forward cautiously, placed his machine guns behind the dikes for covering fire, probed with the riflemen of the lead platoon. There was no fire from the trees or huts, no more booby traps. Two of the huts were burning. As HQ approached there was a wild burst of fire and everyone but Harkness, even Himmlemann, threw himself into the mud. Several individual shots. It all seemed to be coming from near one of the burning huts but no one could tell where it was directed.

"Ammo cache," the captain said. He was standing there looking down at them, not haughtily, almost sympathetically. "Get 'em going, Top. It's only some ammo in the roof cooking off."

"Right."

They moved on in. The lead platoon was set up in a fan around the edges of the clearing where the huts were. Occasional rounds kept popping off in one of the flaming hootches and the burning bamboo made loud cracks, like a small caliber pistol. The lead platoon lieutenant showed them several bunkers, and part of a body. There were several clips for an AK–47 in one of the bunkers. The whole place smelled of explosive, a lingering acrid odor.

Prissholm and Upshaw went to check out a hut at the far corner of the clearing.

"Should we throw a grenade in?" Prissholm asked.

"You fucking idiot," Upshaw said.

"There might be somebody in there."

"You think a goddamn grenade wouldn't blow through these walls and get you too? That's thatch, you asshole, not brick."

Upshaw stood beside the doorway for a few moments, his eyes closed, adjusting them for the dim light inside. Then he pushed through the opening. Along the back wall were bags of rice, gunny sacks filled to the bursting, and several big earthen jars. The hut had been hit many times by shell and rocket fragments, and there were gashes in the thatching that admitted oblongs and sickles of light. Along one wall was a low Vietnamese style bed, a platform of planks covered with reed mats. Lying on it was a figure. Upshaw turned his rifle on it, index finger taking up the slack in the trigger, thumb automatically checking that the fire selector was off safety, in the full auto position, rock 'n roll. Then he saw the figure was a woman, pregnant and dead, a great rip torn in her throat. The blood was still bright. Flies were buzzing in it.

"Go tell the old man we got a greased dink in here."

A few minutes later the captain, Burns and Leyba arrived. As the captain approached the woman seemed to move, twist slightly.

"I thought you said she was zapped?"

"Let me see," Burns said.

"She's pregnant."

"No shit."

Burns was holding her wrist, feeling for pulse.

"She's gone," the medic said.

"She moved," Harkness said. "I saw her."

"Reflex. I think she may have been in labor."

The woman twitched again, rolled slightly. The flies buzzed away from the wound at her throat.

"My God," Harkness said.

Leyba looked quickly at the captain. It was the first time he could remember seeing a crack in his composure, and he had seen him in and after four or five real firefights, seen him any number of times when anyone normal would have been shitting in his pants. Harkness's composure was one of the things Leyba hated about him most.

"Yeah," Burns said. "She's in labor." He pulled away the blanket that covered her legs. "It's coming out."

The medic stood up, wiped his arm across his forehead.

"Christ. I don't know how to handle something like this."

"It's not alive, is it? The baby?"

"I don't know."

"My God."

"Can you call Battalion, sir?"

"What do I say? That I've got a dead woman having a baby?"

"I guess so. Something like that."

"Leyba, let's go outside."

The body moved again.

"I need some forceps. I can't do a fucking thing without big forceps. I ought to have some boiled water too."

"I'll call Battalion."

The captain and Leyba left.

"It can't be alive," Prissholm said.

"It might be. I've never even read anything about a case like this."

"You could write it up, doc," Upshaw said.

Lebya came back in.

"They'll send out a fucking chopper if you want, but the colonel says he hasn't got any forceps. Upshaw, Top wants you."

"I need forceps," Burns said. "I don't think she ought to be moved."

"The old man didn't say anything about getting you any. Only a chopper."

"Because they haven't got any."

"What do you want me to tell the old man?"

"Tell him let me work on her awhile."

Leyba returned, put his radio set down by the door.

"O.K. Only he says don't take too long. We gotta make the next fucking objective."

"Find me some water," Burns said.

The top of the baby's head was showing. Burns was pushing on the women's abdomen. Her contractions were not forceful enough to do any good, he thought.

Leyba discovered that the earthen jars held fresh water, filled his helmet. He stood over the medic watching. It reminded him of once at home, at his family's farm in northern New Mexico. They had had a cow that couldn't calve. His father had not wanted to call the vet, had not wanted to have to pay. The cow had grown weaker and weaker. Finally, when it was obviously going to die if something was not done, his father had tied the cow to the corral gate post, put a rope around the neck of the half born calf. He attached the rope to his saddle and slapped the horse. The calf had been jerked out, its neck broken, but the cow had recovered. He thought of suggesting something like that to Burns, but of course the mother was already dead, and there weren't any horses around.

"It's stuck," Burns said. "I'm going to have to cut."

He stood up again. Sweat was popping out of his forehead. He ought to have boiled water to sterilize his knife at the least, but he didn't think there was time. He drew the knife, a Navy K-bar, an excellent knife that he had traded away from a corpsman for a half pound of good Lao grass. He did not like bayonets, which were what they were issued, because they would not hold an edge. He liked good tools, had promised himself the finest instruments when he got out. He seared the blade with the flame from his zippo.

"That won't sterilize it," Prissholm said. "Lighter fuel is full of grease."

"Shut up, dickhead," Leyba said.

Burns wiped his forehead, knelt, and began to cut. "Throw some water on," he told Leyba.

"Easy. That's enough."

"It ain't bleeding much."

"She's dead. No circulation."

Harkness came in, watched for a moment, and left. Leyba was grinning.

"More water."

Burns worked quickly, but carefully. Once he stopped, wiped the sweat away again. Several times he asked Leyba for water. His first incision was not big enough, the abdominal muscles clamped shut, he could not get hold of the baby.

A crowd gathered outside the hut. Harkness came back, stood just inside the door, prevented the men from pressing in.

"Water."

"That's getting it," Leyba said. "Cut some more sideways."

"Enough water."

The medic pried the slit open, reached in.

"He's taking it out," Leyba said for the benefit of the crowd.

Burns pulled the baby free, tied off the cord with a boot lace, slashed it with the bloody K-bar, and held the form up by the heels in best Ben Casey fashion. He began to slap it.

"It's dead," Leyba said.

"Throw some water on," someone suggested from the door. "Dunk it."

"That's enough," Harkness said.

Burns kept slapping, could not think what else to do, harder now, urgently, as if he could force life into it, but he produced no response. Finally he put it down beside the mother, pulled the blanket over them both. He was still sweating unnaturally, the beads popping out quickly and big on his forehead. He wiped his face on his shirt front, but it was too wet already to absorb much. He felt drained, almost as if he had dysentery. It was the way he always felt after he had lost someone.

"That's it," he said. He started for the door. "That's the ball game."

They formed up, moved through the trees and into the paddies on the other side. There was another treeline barely visible on the horizon.

As they hopped along through the muck Harkness was worried. They had lost a lot of time, would have to press hard to reach the safest position to spend the night. Automatically he checked that the point and flank security was out, that the men were spacing themselves far enough apart.

The war down here was pure shit, he reflected. He had seen more blood spilled in the high country along the border two years ago, but there hadn't been problems with civilians, and up there he'd never seen anything like this today. It had been a cleaner and more honorable war, a soldier's war, with fights between regular units of real armies, without much booby trapping, without the muck and the people. Down here there were limitless complications. It occurred to him that when the enemy came back to the hootches, and they surely would come back, they might take pictures of the woman and child, use them as anti-American propaganda. GI dogs murder pregnant woman, rip infant from womb. If they did that and our own psy war people ever hooked the stuff to his company, he'd have a helluva time explaining what had really happened.

Also, he should have done something about the rice. There had been a ton, maybe more, in that hut. He hadn't even called it in. He had been so involved with the other thing. Next to getting confirmed kills, or weapons, capturing rice was about the best thing that could happen to a commander. He could at least have had the men urinate on the sacks; that was what they did if there was not time or means to haul a cache in. That was a stupid thing to have missed.

Harkness had not had to come back to Vietnam, and he now thought, as he had often the past few months, coming back had been a mistake. After instructing at ranger school he had been an aide to a general at the Pentagon, and the general had been assigned to the mission in Brazil, had wanted to take him along. But he had volunteered to come back here instead. His friends had all come back and he had felt that somehow it was wrong for him not to. The general, he knew, had been disappointed, thought him a fool. He had thought that when he told the old man he'd understand, would pat him on the back, realize that a job in an advisory mission was not like commanding troops in the field, that an infantry officer should always try to be with the men, had an obligation to them and to himself, to his profession, but the general had only shrugged, told him he was sorry. It was not wise to lose the favor of a general, even an obscure brigadier, and Harkness had tried to explain that he'd learn more on a second tour than he had on the first. He might, the general had said, and gave that cold shrug again. Well, learn he had, especially this today, although what you could not say exactly, or what use it would be.

Leyba was feeling better than he had all day, better than at any time since the last stand-down. He figured they'd had their action for a while, he could scratch this day, which left only two more to be lived through. He was even pretty sure he was going to make them. He could not say why, but for the first time in months he really believed he'd get out of it.

Which did not make him feel any more gently toward Harkness. Maybe he felt so good because Harkness was obviously shaken. Next to seeing the bastard dinged, seeing him blow his cool was the best thing he could imagine. He had already mentioned it to Blacksides and Upshaw. In fact, the only things wrong were that he was still here, and the radio was still cutting down into his shoulders.

Prissholm was horribly, terribly thirsty. The back of his throat was the consistency of stale cotton candy. He had drunk his last half canteen and would have to wait for the next break to get some water from someone. He should have filled his canteens from the earthen jars, but he had been too absorbed. Now he thought that he must not think about what had happened, it was another unreal event, another threat to his imperiled sanity, and he must not dwell on it. If he did not think about it, it would not touch him, and he'd be all right. It was like his fraternity initiation, when they had gang-banged the whore hired for the purpose, everyone very drunk, people sitting and standing in the bedroom watching. He had been very drunk and had climbed on himself finally, when there had been no graceful way left to refuse, surprised at his own potency, that he could even be potent in such a situation — degrading and ludicrous — and even during the act telling himself it did not matter unless he let it matter.

And Burns, the good medic, rolled himself a huge joint, a real bomber, a B–52. He needed it, the real thing, with no menthol or tobacco or filter to cut its effect. He had tried to slip back into his daydream, reconjure the Loach and the house on the cliff and the surf, but he was too tired to make his mind go the way he wanted it to, to force out the woman and the cutting and the slapping, the defeat, so he reached into the side of his bag where he kept morphine and his cache of grass and papers, and stopped on an especially firm clump of rice, standing in plain sight of Harkness and Top Sergeant Himmlemann and anyone else who wanted to look, not really giving a damn, and rolled his bomber, and lit up. No one even cast a curious glance.